Code of Practice for the construction, machinery, equipment, stability and survey of sail training ships between 7 metres and 24 metres in length

GW00771250

Marine Directorate 1990

LONDON: HMSO

ISBN 0 11 550955 0

Contents

1 Foreword

This Code of Practice is intended to be applied to United Kingdom mono-hulled sailing ships of 7 metres in length and over but less than 24 metres in length which are engaged at sea in sail training activities on a commercial basis. Such activities include any duties undertaken by members of the crew, whether performed under instruction or not, associated with sailing or operation of the ship, for which payment is either made or received. It should be noted, however, that the classification of any United Kingdom ship is very much dependent upon the terms on which those persons forming the crew have been appointed. It is therefore important to study the contents of Merchant Shipping Notice No. M 1194, which is reproduced in Annex 5. In addition a note giving an interpretation by counsel and used by the Department, of the term 'pleasure yacht', is at Annex 6.

It is considered that the standards contained in this Code represent good practice and that they should be taken into account, as appropriate, when considering all sail training ships including multi-hulled ships and ships of less than 7 metres in length. At this stage, however, it is not possible to comment upon the suitability of applying the stability standards to multi-hulled ships. Such standards will be considered when the Code is reviewed.

United Kingdom sail training ships are normally required to comply with various Merchant Shipping Rules and Regulations. Compliance with the standards required by this Code, however, would constitute sufficient grounds for exemption from those Rules and Regulations, wherever appropriate. The form of the General Exemption which has been issued for this purpose is reproduced at Annex 16.

The Code was developed by the Marine Directorate of the Department of Transport in collaboration with a Working Group following a period of public consultation. The membership of this Working Group was as follows:

Association of Sea Training Organisations	Commander M W Kemmis Betty
	Mr J H Hamilton

The primary aim in developing this Code has been to set standards of safety and protection for all who put to sea in sail training ships and particularly for those who are trainees. The level of safety it prescribes is considered to be commensurate with the current expectations of the general public. The Code relates specially to the construction of the ship, its machinery, equipment and stability. In addition, however, designers and builders will need to pay special regard to the intended area of operation and the working conditions to which the ship will be subjected when selecting the materials and equipment to be used in its construction.

In addition, the Code deals with the equally important subject of manning and of the qualifications needed for the senior members of the crew.

The Working Group recognised that the Code may need to be revised in due course in the light of experience gained in its use. At that time consideration will also be given to making the Code the subject of a Statutory Instrument.

The builder, owner or operator of the ship should take all reasonable measures to ensure that any material or appliance fitted in accordance with the requirements of this Code is suitable for the purpose intended, having regard to its location in the ship, the area of operation and the weather conditions which may be encountered.

Where equipment manufacturered in accordance with a British, European or International standard is required by this Code, the Sail Training Ship Certifying Authority may, for a limited period, accept existing equipment which can be shown to be of equivalent standard. When such equipment is replaced, the replacement should be to an acceptable standard.

It is important to stress that, whilst all reasonable measures have been taken to develop standards which will result in the production of safe and seaworthy sailing ships, total safety at sea can never be guaranteed. As a consequence it is most strongly recommended that the owner or operator of every sailing ship takes out a policy of insurance for all persons contracted to form part of the ship's complement. Such a policy should be formulated to give proper and adequate financial cover in respect of the risks of personal sickness, injury or death whilst on board the ship.

2 Definitions

In this Code:

"Authorised Surveyor" means a surveyor member or an associate surveyor member nominated by the Yacht Brokers, Designers and Surveyors Association or any person who by reason of relevant professional qualifications, practical experience or expertise is authorised by one of the Sail Training Ship Certifying Authorities listed in the Code to carry out the surveys and inspections required by Section 27 of the Code;

"Efficient" in relation to a fitting, piece of equipment or material means that all reasonable and practicable measures have been taken to ensure that it is suitable for the purpose for which it is intended to be used;

"Existing sail training ship" means any sail training ship which is not a new sail training ship;

"Freeboard" means the distance measured vertically downwards from the lowest point of the upper edge of the Weather Deck to the waterline in still water;

"Length" means the overall length from the foreside of the foremost fixed permanent structure to the aftside of the aftermost fixed permanent structure of the ship;

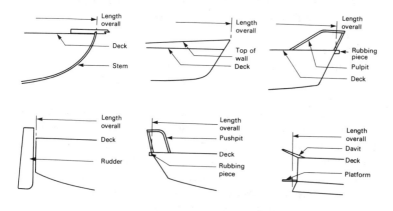

"New sail training ship" means any ship intended to be used
as a sail training ship the keel of which was laid or the
construction or lay-up was started on or after 1 January 1991
or an existing ship not already being a sail training ship but
obtained and newly used as a sail training ship on or after
that date;

"Partially smooth waters" means, as respects any period
specified in Schedule 2 to the Merchant Shipping (Smooth
and Partially Smooth Waters) Rules 1977 the waters of any of
the areas specified in Column 3 of that Schedule in relation
to that period;

"Sail Training Ship Certifying Authority" means one of the
organisations authorised by the Marine Directorate of the
Department of Transport to:
    (a) appoint surveyors for the purpose of surveying and
inspecting sail training ships and issuing and signing
Declarations of Surveys for a Sail Training Ship; and
    (b) issue Sail Training Ship Certificates.

The organisations so authorised by the Department are as
follows:

Lloyd's Register of Shipping
Bureau Veritas
American Bureau of Shipping
Det Norske Veritas
Germanischer Lloyd
The Royal Yachting Association;

"Smooth waters" means any waters not being the sea or
partially smooth waters and in particular means waters of any
of the areas specified in Column 2 of the Schedule to the
Merchant Shipping (Smooth and Partially Smooth Waters)
Regulations 1987 (SI 1987/1591);

"To sea" means beyond the partially smooth waters, or
smooth waters if there are no partially smooth waters, as
defined in the Merchant Shipping (Smooth and Partially
Smooth Waters) Regulations 1987;

"Watertight" means capable of preventing the passage of
water in either direction;

"Weather Deck" means the main deck which is exposed to the elements;

"Weathertight" means capable of preventing the admission of a significant quantity of water into the ship when subjected to a hose test.

3 Application and Interpretation

3.1 Application

Any ship used as a sail training ship on or after 1 January 1991 should comply with the appropriate requirements of this Code. The Code is intended to apply to all United Kingdom mono-hulled sailing ships other than pleasure yachts (see Annex 6) of 7 metres or more in length but less than 24 metres in length which proceed to sea, do not carry cargo and are used for sail training activities of a commercial nature except that the Code does not apply to ships carrying fewer than 15 persons on voyages in the course of which they are at no time more than 15 miles from the point of departure, exclusive of any smooth waters, nor more than 3 miles from land.

3.2 Interpretation

Where any question of interpretation of any part of this Code arises an opinion may be obtained on written application to the Deputy Surveyor General 1 who may consult the organisations listed in the foreword as deemed appropriate.

4 Construction & Structural Strength

4.1 General Requirements

All ships should be fitted with a watertight Weather Deck and be of adequate structural strength to withstand the sea and weather conditions likely to be encountered in the intended area of operation.

4.2 Structural Strength

4.2.1 *New Sail Training Ships*

New ships will be considered to be of adequate strength if built;

(a) in accordance with the hull certification standards for small craft set by any of the following bodies; Lloyd's Register of Shipping; Bureau Veritas; American Bureau of Shipping; Det Norske Veritas, and Germanischer Lloyd; or

(b) in general accordance with the standards of any sailing ship which has a history of safe operation in an area where the sea and weather conditions are no less severe than those likely to be encountered in the intended area of operation.

New ships not built in accordance with sub-paragraphs (a) or (b) may be specially considered provided that full information, including calculations, drawings and details of materials is presented to the surveyor appointed by the Sail Training Ship Certifying Authority.

4.2.2 *Existing Sail Training Ships*

Existing ships will be considered to be of adequate structural strength if they are in a good state of repair and are;

(a) built to one of the standards prescribed in para 4.2.1 for new ships, or

(b) of a design with a record of at least 5 years' history of safe operation in an area where the sea and weather conditions are no less severe than those likely to be encountered in the intended area of operation.

4.3 Decks

All sail training ships should have a watertight Weather Deck which extends from stem to stern. The Weather Deck may be stepped, recessed or raised provided the stepped, recessed or raised portion is of watertight construction.

4.3.1 *Recesses*

Any recess in the weather deck should be of watertight construction and have;

(a) a volume (V_c) which does not exceed the value obtained from the following formula;

$$V_c = 10\% \text{ (length of ship} \times \text{breadth of ship} \times \text{freeboard abreast the cockpit (or recess))},$$

(b) means of drainage capable of operating at 30° angle of heel; such drainage to have an effective area, excluding grills and baffles, of at least 10cm^2.

If the recess is provided with lockers which give direct access to the interior of the hull, such lockers should be fitted with weather-tight covers. In addition the covers to lockers should be permanently attached to the ship's structure and fitted with at least two locking devices to secure them in the fully closed position.

4.4   Watertight Bulkheads (ships carrying 15 or more berthed persons)

4.4.1   *New Sail Training Ships*

When these ships are intended to carry 15 or more berthed persons they should be constructed in accordance with the following requirements, except that consideration will be given to the continued acceptance of existing designs which are part of an existing building programme:

(a) the ship should be so arranged that the flooding of any one compartment will not cause the ship to float at a waterline which is less than 75 mm below the Weather Deck at any point. Standard permeabilities should be used in this assessment;

(It is recommended that in the flooded condition the residual stability should be such that any angle of equilibrium does not exceed 7 degrees from the upright, the resulting righting lever curve has a range of at least 15 degrees beyond any angle of equilibrium, the maximum righting lever within that range is not less than 100 mm and the area under the curve is not less than 0.015 metre radians. At intermediate stages of flooding the maximum righting lever should be at least 50 mm with a range of positive righting levels of at least 7 degrees)

(b) where pipes, cables, etc penetrate watertight bulkheads they should be provided with valves and watertight glands as appropriate. Doorways fitted in watertight bulkheads should be of watertight construction and be kept closed at sea at the master's discretion.

4.4.2 *Existing Sail Training Ships*

In the case of existing ships intended to carry 15 or more berthed persons, it is most strongly recommended that modifications in accordance with para. 4.4.1 be implemented as appropriate when the ship undergoes major structural alterations.

5 Weathertight Integrity

All ships should be designed and constructed in a manner which will prevent the ready ingress of sea water and in particular comply with the following requirements.

5.1 Hatchways and Skylight Hatches

5.1.1 *General requirement*

All hatchways which give access to spaces below the Weather Deck should be of efficient construction and be provided with efficient weathertight means of closure. Covers to hatches should be hinged, sliding, or permanently secured by other equivalent means to the structure of the ship and be provided with at least two locking devices to enable them to be firmly secured in the closed position.

All hatchways with hinged covers which are located in the forward portion of the ship should normally have the hinges fitted to the forward side of the hatch.

5.1.2 *Hatchways which are open at sea*

In general, hatches should be kept closed at sea. However, hatchways other than those referred to in paragraph 5.2.2 which are to be kept open for lengthy periods at sea should be kept as small as practicable, but never more than 1 sq.m in clear area. Such hatchways should be located on the centre line of the ship or as close thereto as is practicable. These hatches should be fitted such that the access opening is at least 300 mm (12″) above the top of the adjacent weather deck at side.

5.2 Doorways and Companionways

5.2.1 *Doorways located above the Weather Deck*

Doorways located above the Weather Deck which give access to spaces below should be provided with weathertight doors. Such doors should be of efficient construction, permanently and strongly attached to the bulkhead, open outwards and have efficient means of closure which can be operated from either side. They should be located as close as practicable to the centre line of the ship but if located in the sides of a house they should be hinged on the forward edge. Such doorways should be provided with a coaming the top of which is at least 300 mm (12") above the Weather Deck. Coamings may be portable, provided they are permanently secured to the structure of the ship with keep chains or lanyards and can be locked firmly in position.

5.2.2 *Companion Hatch Openings*

Companion hatch openings from recessed cockpits which give access to spaces below the Weather Deck should be fitted with a coaming the top of which is at least 300 mm (12") above the cockpit sole. If washboards are used to close the vertical opening they should be so arranged and fitted that they will not become dislodged in the event of a capsize. The maximum breadth of the opening in a companion hatch should not exceed 1 metre.

5.3 Skylights

All skylights should be of efficient weathertight construction and should be located on the centre line of the ship or as near thereto as practicable. If they are of the opening type they should be provided with efficient means whereby they can be secured in the closed position.

Unless the glazing material and its method of fixing in the frame is equivalent in strength to the structure in which it is fitted, portable covers should be provided which can be efficiently secured in place in the event of breakage.

5.4 Portlights

Portlights to spaces below the Weather Deck or in steps, recesses, raised deck structures, deckhouses or superstructures protecting openings leading below the Weather Deck should be of efficient construction and fitted with permanently attached deadlights capable of being closed weathertight. Opening type portlights should not exceed 250 mm (10″) in diameter. No opening type portlights should be fitted in the hull below the Weather Deck.

5.5 Windows

If windows are to be fitted in the main hull below the Weather Deck they should be equivalent in size, strength and weathertight integrity to a portlight. Unless the glazing material and its method of fixing in the frame is equivalent in strength to the structure in which it is fitted, portable covers should be provided, at the rate of 50% for each size of window, which can be efficiently secured in place in the event of breakage.

If windows are to be fitted in spaces above the Weather Deck or in the sides of a cockpit or recess they should be of efficient weathertight construction. Portable covers should be provided, at the rate of 50% for each size of window, which can be efficiently secured in place in the event of breakage.

5.6 Ventilators

Ventilators should be of efficient construction and provided with a permanently attached means of weathertight closure. They should be kept as far inboard as practicable and have a coaming of sufficient height to prevent the ready admission of water. Ventilators which must be kept open, e.g. for the supply of air to machinery or for the discharge of noxious or flammable gases, should be specially considered as regards their location and height above deck.

5.7 Air pipes

Air pipes greater than 10 mm in diameter serving fuel or other tanks should be of efficient construction and be provided with a permanently attached means of weathertight closure. Where located on the Weather Deck they should be kept as far inboard as practicable and have a coaming of sufficient height to prevent inadvertent flooding.

5.8 Sea Inlets and Discharges

All openings below the Weather Deck should be provided with an efficient means of closure. Where the opening is for the purpose of an inlet or discharge below the waterline it should be fitted with a seacock, valve or other effective means of closure which is readily accessible in an emergency. Where the opening is for a log or any other sensor which is capable of being withdrawn it should be fitted in an efficient watertight manner and provided with an effective means of closure when such fitting is removed. The discharge pipes from water closets should be looped up within the hull, to the underside of deck.

5.9 Materials for valves and associated piping

Valves and similar fittings attached to the ship's side below the waterline within engine spaces or other high fire risk areas should be of steel, bronze, or other material having a similar resistance to impact and fire. The associated pipes should, in areas where a high risk of fire exists, be of steel, bronze, copper or other equivalent material. If, in other areas, plastic piping is to be used it should be of good quality and of a type suitable for the intended purpose.

6 Water Freeing Arrangements

6.1 Where a deck is fitted with bulwarks such that shipped water may be temporarily trapped behind them, the bulwarks should be provided with an adequate number of freeing ports. The area of such freeing ports should be at least 10 per cent of that part of the bulwark area which extends for 2/3 of the ship's length amidships and be located in the lower third of the bulwark height, as close to the deck as practicable. The freeing port should be fitted with a grid having a spacing of not more than 50 mm (2″) in each direction fitted across it. If shutters are fitted to freeing ports they should have sufficient clearance to prevent jamming and the shutter hinges should have pins or bearings of non-corrodible material.

6.2 Structures and spaces considered to be non-weathertight should be provided with efficient drainage arrangements.

7 Machinery

7.1 Every ship should be fitted with a diesel engine and a sufficient supply of fuel capable of propelling it in settled weather and in a calm sea at a speed in knots equal to 1.81 times the square root of the waterline length in metres (the square root of the waterline length in feet) or 6 knots, whichever is less, for a period of at least 24 hours.

7.2 The machinery, fuel tanks and associated piping systems and fittings should be of a design and construction adequate for the service for which they are intended and should be so installed and protected as to reduce to a minimum any danger to persons on board, due regard being paid to moving parts, hot surfaces and other hazards.

7.3 The engine should be provided with either mechanical or handstarting or electric starting with independent batteries. If the sole means of starting is by battery, the battery should be in duplicate and connected to the starter motor via a 'change over switch' so that either battery can be used for starting the engine. Charging facilities for the batteries should be available.

7.4 Main propulsion machinery and all auxiliary machinery essential to the propulsion and the safety of the ship should, as fitted in the ship, be designed to operate when the ship is upright and when inclined at any angle of heel up to and including 15 degrees either way under static conditions and 22.5 degrees either way under dynamic conditions (rolling) and simultaneously inclined dynamically (pitching) 7.5 degrees by bow or stern.

7.5 Portable containers used for the stowage of petrol should be clearly marked and should be stowed on the upper deck where they can readily be jettisoned and where spillage will drain overboard. The number of such containers should be kept to a minimum.

8 Electrical Arrangements

8.1 Electrical arrangements should be such as to minimise risk of fire and electric shock. Particular attention should be paid to the provision of overload and short circuit protection of all circuits, except engine starting circuits, supplied from batteries.

8.2   Where general lighting within the ship is provided by a centralised electrical system, an alternative source of lighting, sufficient to enable persons to make their way up to the open deck, should be provided.

8.3   Ventilation should be provided to minimise the accumulation of any gas which might be emitted from batteries.

9   Steering Gear

9.1   All ships should be provided with efficient means of steering.

9.2   Where the steering gear is fitted with remote control, arrangements should be made for emergency steering in the event of failure of such control. Such arrangements may take the form of a tiller to fit the head of the rudder stock.

9.3   The control position should be located so that the person conning the ship has a clear view ahead.

10   Bilge Pumping

10.1   All ships carrying 15 or more persons or ships of 15 metres in length and over should have an efficient bilge pumping system consisting of at least one hand bilge pump and one engine driven or independent power bilge pump with suction pipes so arranged that any compartment can be drained when the ship is heeled up to an angle of 10 degrees. Every bilge pump suction line should be fitted with an efficient strum box.

All other ships should be provided with at least two hand bilge pumps, one situated in the cockpit or on the Weather Deck and one in the accommodation. Both hand bilge pumps must be capable of being operated with all hatchways and companionways closed.

10.2   Where propulsion machinery is fitted in an enclosed watertight compartment which is unmanned at any time, a bilge level alarm should be fitted. The alarm should provide an audible warning in the Master's cabin or for the Engineer as appropriate and at the control position.

11   Stability

11.1   New Sail Training Ships

The standard of stability to be achieved by new ships will be dependent upon their length. Ships of 15 metres in length and over should comply with the standards given in para 11.1.1 and ships of less than 15 metres in length should comply with the standards given in para 11.1.2.

11.1.1   *Ships of 15 metres in length and over*

   (a) The centre of gravity (KG) of the ship should be established by an inclining experiment and curves of statical stability (GZ curves) calculated for the following conditions should be produced:
      (i) loaded departure, 100% consumables
      (ii) loaded arrival, 10% consumables.

NOTE: The above conditions may include a margin for growth not exceeding 5% of the lightweight with the VCG positioned at the upper deck amidships.

   (b) The GZ curves required by sub-paragraphs (a)(i) and (a)(ii) above should have a positive range of not less than the angle determined by the formula in the table in para 11.1.2.6.

   (c) In addition to the requirements of paragraph (b) the angle of steady heel obtained from the intersection of a "derived wind heeling lever" curve with either of the GZ curves referred to in sub paragraph (a) above should be greater than 15 degrees (see Figure 1).

In fig.1
'DWHL'   = the "derived wind heeling lever" at any angle θ degrees.
                 $= 0.5 \times WLO \times Cos^{1.3}\,\theta$
                 where $WLO = \dfrac{GZf}{Cos^{1.3}\,\theta f}$

FIGURE 1

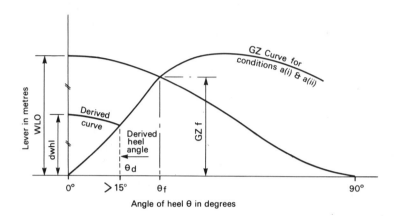

Angle of heel θ in degrees

Noting that: WLO is the magnitude of the actual wind heeling lever at 0 degrees which would cause the ship to heel to the 'down flooding angle' (θf) or 60 degrees whichever is least,

GZf –   is the lever of the ship's GZ curve at the 'down flooding angle' (θf) or 60 degrees whichever is least,

θd –   is the angle at which the 'derived wind heeling' curve intersects the GZ curve. (If θd is less than 15 degrees the ship will be considered as having insufficient stability for the purpose of this Code).

θf –   the 'down flooding angle' is deemed to occur when openings having an *aggregate area,* in square metres, greater than;

$$\frac{\text{ship's displacement in tonnes,}}{1500}$$

are immersed.

Moreover, it is the angle at which the lower edge of the actual opening which *results* in critical flooding becomes immersed. All

16

openings regularly used for crew access and for ventilation should be considered when determining the downflooding angle. No opening regardless of size which may lead to progressive flooding should be immersed at an angle of heel of less than 40 degrees. Air pipes to tanks can, however, be disregarded.

If as a result of immersion of openings in a deckhouse a ship cannot meet the required standard those deckhouse openings may be ignored and the openings in the Weather Deck used instead to determine θf. In such cases the GZ curve should be derived without the benefit of the buoyancy of the deckhouse.

It might be noted that provided the ship complies with the requirements of (a), (b) and (c) above and it is sailed with an angle of heel which is no greater than the 'derived angle of heel', it should be capable of withstanding a wind gust equal to 1.4 times the actual wind velocity (ie twice the actual wind pressure) without immersing the 'down flooding openings', or heeling to an angle greater than 60 degrees.

(d) A 'stability information booklet' based on the Department's model booklet should be placed on board. This booklet should include details of the maximum steady angle of heel for the worst sailing condition. The steady angle of heel is to be calculated in accordance with subparagraph (c) above. The booklet should also include curves of maximum recommended steady angle of heel for the prevention of down flooding in the event of squall conditions. Details of the development of such curves are given in the Department's Model Stability Information Booklet for Sail Training Ships.

11.1.2 Ships of less than 15 metres in length

11.1.2.1 *General*

The stability of these ships should be determined by the methods discussed below and their areas of operation should be dependent upon the standards which they are shown to achieve.

17

11.1.2.2 Ships without external ballast keels

(a) *Stability assessment*
The centre of gravity (KG) of the ship should be established by an inclining experiment and, in addition, curves of statical stability (GZ curves) for the following conditions shall be produced:
  (i) loaded departure, 100% consumables
  (ii) loaded arrival, 10% consumables
NOTE: The above conditions may include a margin for growth not exceeding 5% of the lightweight with the V.C.G. positioned at the upper deck amidships.

(b) *Permitted area of operation*
The permitted area of operation is dependent upon the ship's range of stability as indicated in the table in para. 11.1.2.6.

11.1.2.3 Ships fitted with external ballast keels

(a) The stability assessment of these ships may be determined by any one of the following methods:
  (i) Method 1 – as for ships without external ballast keels, see paragraph 11.1.2.2(a) above;
  (ii) Method 2 – by the formula shown in paragraph 11.1.2.4;
  (iii) Method 3 – by the 'STOPS' Numeral developed by the Royal Yachting Association (RYA) and discussed in paragraph 11.1.2.5.

(b) *Permitted area of operation*
The permitted area of operation is dependent upon the ship's range of stability or its STOPS Numeral as indicated in the table in para. 11.1.2.6.

11.1.2.4 Formula for estimating range of stability

The range of positive stability for ships fitted with external ballast keels may be estimated from the following formula

$$\text{ESTIMATED RANGE} = 110 + \frac{400}{(SV - 10.0)} \text{ degrees}$$

Where $SV = \dfrac{\text{Beam}^2}{BR \times DCB \times (\text{DISPLACED VOL})^{\frac{1}{3}}}$

Noting that:–

Beam = greatest beam measured excluding rubbing strips, in metres.

Ballast Ratio (BR) = weight of ballast in tonnes contained in the keel divided by the full displacement in tonnes.

Displaced Volume = the volume of the ship's displacement, in m^3, at the operational draught.

Draught of canoe body (DCB) in metres is taken by measuring the maximum draught at the 1/8 of the full beam from the centreline as follows:

FIGURE 2

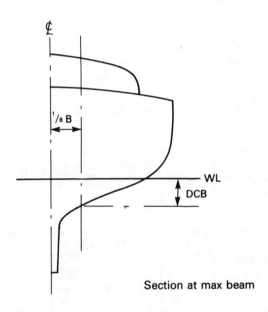

Section at max beam

Once the estimated range of stability has been determined it is necessary to study the table in paragraph 11.1.2.6 to ascertain the area of operation which the range permits.

11.1.2.5 *Assessment using the RYA 'STOPS' numeral or use of SSS numeral calculated by the Royal Ocean Racing Club*

(a) Ships can have their area of operation based upon the RYA 'STOPS Numeral'.

19

The derivation of the STOPS numeral is explained in Annex 13.

Once the STOPS Numeral has been determined it is necessary to study the table in paragraph 11.1.2.6 to ascertain the permitted area of operation.

(b) A SSS numeral calculated by the RORC will be accepted in place of a STOPS numeral, provided that it includes a self righting factor based on an inclining experiment and shown on a valid IOR or IMS rating certificate.

11.1.2.6 *Table showing permitted areas of operation and STOPS numeral for ships less than 15 metres in length*

| Permitted area of operation | Code category | Minimum required standards | |
		Range of stability (degrees)	STOPS numeral
Unrestricted	0	$90 + 60 \times \dfrac{(24 - LOA)}{17}$	50
Extended European Operating Area	1	$90 + 60 \times \dfrac{(24 - LOA)}{17}$	40
Near Continental Operating Area and Mediterranean & Black Seas	2	$90 + 60 \times \dfrac{(24 - LOA)}{20}$	30
Within 15 miles of coast of country of operation	3	$90 + 60 \times \dfrac{(24 - LOA)}{25}$	20

The geographical limits of the 'areas of operation' are described in paragraph 11.1.2.7

11.1.2.7 *Permitted areas of operation – Geographical limits*

CATEGORY 0   UNRESTRICTED

CATEGORY 1   EXTENDED EUROPEAN OPERATING AREA (this is the same as the EXTENDED EUROPEAN TRADING AREA: (See Appendix A of Annex 7))

CATEGORY 2   NEAR CONTINENTAL OPERATING AREA which is within the area bounded by a line from a point on the Norwegian coast in latitude 62° North to a point 62° North 02° West; thence to a point 58° North, 10° West; thence to a point 51° North 12° West; thence to Brest, but excluding all waters which lie to the eastward of a line drawn between Kristiansand, Norway and Hanstholm lighthouse on the North Danish coast, except between the dates of 1st May and 30th September. AND IN ADDITION THE MEDITERRANEAN AND BLACK SEAS

CATEGORY 3   WITHIN 15 MILES OF COAST OF COUNTRY OF OPERATION.

11.1.2.8 *Stability information for ships less than 15 metres in length*

Stability information will not be required in booklet form for these ships. The owner should, however, present documentary evidence to show that the required range of stability or STOPS Numeral is in accordance with the table in Section 11.1.2.6 for the intended and permitted areas of operation.

11.1.2.9 *Guidance on stability assessment*

It should be noted that certifying authorities may require a full stability analysis for any vessel which has been modified from the original design, particularly if the freeboard has been significantly reduced or the modification has involved the addition of a mast-furled main sail, a roller-reefing

FIGURE 3

NEAR CONTINENTAL OPERATING AREA AND
THE MEDITERRANEAN AND BLACK SEAS

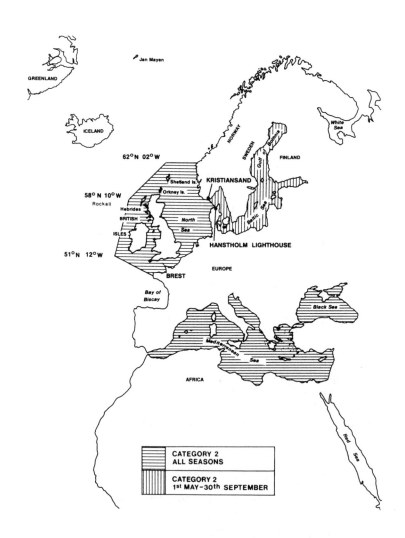

FIGURE 4

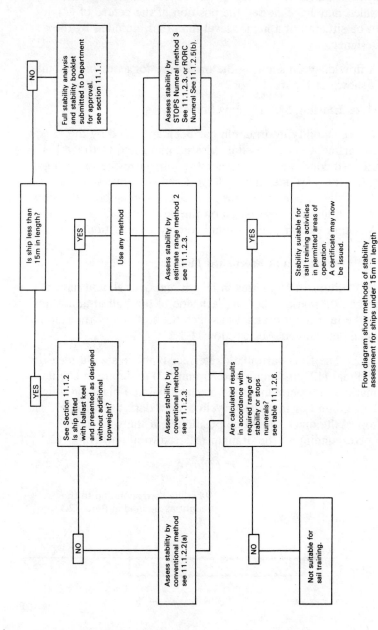

Flow diagram show methods of stability assessment for ships under 15m in length

23

headsail, a radar antenna or any other item of equipment which may have caused the position of the centre of gravity to be situated at a higher level than that intended by the designer.

A flow diagram showing the procedure for assessing stability is shown at Figure 4.

11.2   Existing Sail Training Ships

Where stability information has been approved by the Department under existing criteria, published October 1987, this will continue to be acceptable subject to the following:
   (a) the ship does not undergo a major conversion; or
   (b) the owner or organisation elects to re-submit the ship for stability approval based on the new criteria.
All other existing ships should comply with section 11.1.

12   Freeboard and Freeboard Marking

12.1   Ships of 15 metres in length and over should have a freeboard mark placed on each side of the hull at amidships at the maximum draught at which the stability of the ship has been determined. See Section 11.1.1.

12.2   The freeboard mark referred to above should measure 300 mm (12″) in length and 25 mm (1″) in depth. It should be marked in a permanent manner and painted black on a light background or in white or yellow on a dark background. The top of the mark should be positioned at the waterline corresponding to the draught referred to in paragraph 12.1.

Figure 5

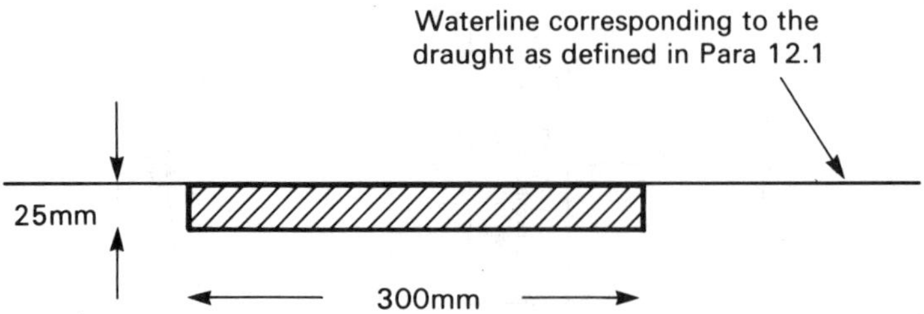

Waterline corresponding to the
draught as defined in Para 12.1

25mm

300mm

12.3   A ship should not operate in any condition which will result in its freeboard marks being submerged when it is at rest and upright in calm water.

13   Life-Saving Appliances

13.1   Life-saving appliances should be provided either in accordance with the requirements for a Class XI ship as specified in the Merchant Shipping (Life Saving Appliances) Regulations 1986, SI 1986/1066, or as described in Annex 1. Liferafts, hydrostatic release units and gas inflatable lifejackets should be serviced annually at a service station approved by the manufacturer. Orally inflated lifejackets should be pressure tested annually, and, as far as reasonable and practicable, visually examined weekly by the operator to determine that they are safe to use.

13.2   Except as otherwise provided in Annex 1, life-saving appliances should be of a type which has been approved by the Department of Transport.

14   Structural Fire Protection

14.1   New Sail Training Ships

14.1.1   The engine should be separated from accommodation spaces and storerooms. The boundary of the engine space should be arranged so as to retain the fire extinguishing medium. Portlights and windows should not be fitted in the boundary of the engine space except that an observation port having a maximum diameter of 150 mm may be fitted in the boundary provided that the frame of the port is of steel or equivalent construction and is fitted with a permanently fixed cover with fastening arrangements. Only toughened safety glass should be used in the observation port.

When the ship is constructed of wood, the exposed surfaces within the engine space should be treated with a flame retardant compound having a Class 1 surface spread of flame rating when tested in accordance with British Standard 476: Part 7: 1971 (or as amended) or coated with an intumescent paint.

When the ship is constructed of fibre reinforced plastic (FRP) or glass reinforced plastic (GRP) flame retardant additives should be incorporated in the exposed layer of resin within the engine space or the final layer of hull lay-up should be of woven rovings. When either of these has not been done, the application of an intumescent paint may be accepted as providing equivalent protection.

Any thermal or acoustic insulation fitted inside the engine space should be non-combustible or should be a polyester high resilient foam or have fire resisting properties similar to such a foam.

Unless a fixed fire extinguishing system is fitted in the engine space, provision should be made in the boundary of the space for discharging fire extinguishing medium into it.

Provision should be made to retain any oil leakage within the confines of the engine space which, in ships constructed of wood, should also prevent absorption of oil into the structure.

14.1.2   Any materials, including surface finishes, which are in the vicinity of open flame cooking and heating devices within the ranges defined in the figure in Annex 3 should comply with the following requirements:

(a) Only non-combustible materials should be used within Range I as indicated in the figure in Annex 3 except that these materials may be faced with any surface finish having a Class 1 surface spread of flame rating when tested in accordance with British Standard 476: Part 7: 1971 or as amended.

(b) Surface finishes within Range II as indicated in the figure in Annex 3 should have a Class 1 surface spread of flame rating. In the case of ships built of FRP or GRP, flame retardant additives incorporated in the exposed layer of resin or the final layer of hull lay-up being of woven roving or the application of an intumescent paint may be accepted as providing equivalent protection. Alternatively, on any ship, the surfaces within Range II may be covered with non-combustible board type material or sheet metal which may be unfaced or faced with a surface finish having a Class 1 surface spread of flame rating.

(c) Curtains or any other suspended textile materials should not be fitted within Ranges I or II as indicated in the figure in Annex 3 unless they satisfy the requirements of (a) or (b) respectively.

LPG installations for cooking or any other purposes should comply with Merchant Shipping Notice No M 984 which is reproduced at Annex 4.

14.1.3   Only Combustion Modified High Resilient (CMHR) foams should be used in upholstered furniture and mattresses. Upholstery fabrics should satisfy the cigarette and butane flame tests of British Standard 5852: Part 1: 1979.

14.1.4   Each accommodation space should be provided, as far as is practicable, with two means of escape.

14.1.5   Smoke detectors should be fitted in the engine space and the space containing the galley range except that this need not apply to ships carrying fewer than 15 persons.

14.2   Existing Ships

Sub-section 14.1 applies to existing ships subject to the following:
   (a) paragraphs 14.1.1 and 14.1.2 should be carried out as soon as possible and not later than 1 January 1992;
   (b) any thermal or acoustic foam insulation fitted inside the engine space of a type other than those referred to in paragraph 14.1.1 should be considered to be equivalent if it is coated with an intumescent paint or compound which is compatible with the foam and provides protection against fire in the engine space; and
   (c) the implementation of paragraph 14.1.3 may be delayed until replacement of existing upholstery or mattresses becomes necessary.

15   Fire Appliances

15.1   Every ship should be provided with efficient fire fighting equipment in accordance with Annex 2.

15.2   A valve or cock which is capable of being closed from a position outside the engine space should be fitted in the fuel feed pipe as close as is practicable to the fuel tank.

16   Radio Equipment

16.1   Radio Installation

16.1.1   Every ship should carry equipment for transmitting

and receiving on the VHF Maritime Mobile band and for receiving 198 kHz. When the main aerial is fitted to the mast an emergency aerial should be provided.

16.1.2 Every ship, other than:
(i) those operating within 30 miles of the coast, or
(ii) those operating within the Limited European Trading Area, the Mediterranean Sea and the Black Sea should be provided with a radio installation capable of transmitting and receiving messages to and from the nearest radio communication centre on land.

The benefit gained by the availability of effective vocal radio-communication with shore facilities in an urgency situation is self-evident. Having regard to the range limitations of VHF the Department recommends that radio equipment is provided which has a range capability commensurate with that needed for the intended voyage.

16.1.3 Where the electrical supply for the radio equipment is from a battery, charging facilities, or a duplicate battery of capacity sufficient for the voyage, should be provided.

16.1.4 A card or cards giving a clear summary of the radiotelephone distress, urgency and safety procedures should be displayed in full view of the radiotelephone operating positions. Guidance as to the format of suitable cards is given in Merchant Shipping Notice No. M.1119.

16.2 EPIRBS

16.2.1 Every ship, except those referred to in paragraph 16.2.2 and 16.2.3, should carry a satellite emergency position-indicating radio beacon (EPIRB) capable of transmitting in the 406 MHz band. EPIRBs should comply with the performance specification MPT 1259 and should be installed in an easily accessible position ready to be manually released, capable of being placed in the liferaft, and capable of floating free if the ship sinks and of being automatically activated.

16.2.2 Every ship carrying fewer than 15 persons, or which is less than 15 metres in length should, after 1st August 1993, carry an EPIRB. This EPIRB may be, instead of the type specified in paragraph 16.2.1, of a type which complies with the performance specification MPT 1278 and be so stowed that it can be rapidly placed in a liferaft.

16.2.3   Ships which do not proceed more than 15 miles from land need not carry the EPIRB referred to in paragraph 16.2.1 and 16.2.2.

17   Navigation Lights, Shapes and Sound Signals

17.1   Every ship should comply with the requirements of the Merchant Shipping (Distress Signals and Prevention of Collisions) Regulations 1989 SI 1798/1989. Lights and sound signals should be type approved by the Department. If it can be demonstrated to the Sail Training Ship Certifying Authority that full compliance with the requirements for sound signals on a particular ship is impracticable the Department will consider granting an exemption as appropriate.

17.2   It should be noted that sailing ships to which this Code refers should be equipped with navigation lights, shapes and sound signals to meet the requirements for both power-driven ships and sailing ships.

18   Navigational Equipment

18.1   Every ship should be fitted with an efficient magnetic compass complying with the following requirements as appropriate:

18.1.1   On steel ships it should be possible to correct the compass for co-efficients B, C and D and heeling error.

18.1.2   The magnetic compass or a repeater should be so positioned as to be clearly readable by the helmsman at the main steering position and fitted with an electric light.

18.1.3   Means should be provided for taking bearings as nearly as practicable over an arc of the horizon of 360°. This requirement may be met by the fitting of a pelorus or, on ships other than steel ships, a hand bearing compass.

18.2   Every ship should be provided with:
(a) a radio navigation system appropriate for the area of operation;
(b) an echo sounder;
(c) a distance measuring log.

19   Miscellaneous Equipment

19.1   Nautical Publications

19.1.1   Every ship of 12 metres or more in length should comply with the requirements of the Merchant Shipping (Carriage of Nautical Publications) Rules 1975 SI 700/1975.

19.1.2   Every ship of less than 12 metres in length to which the requirements of paragraph 19.1.1 do not apply should carry up to date charts, sailing directions, tide tables, tidal stream atlases, and a list of radio signals appropriate for the intended voyage and a copy of the International Code of Signals. These items may be contained in a Nautical Almanac.

19.2   Signalling Lamp

Every ship should be provided with an efficient waterproof electric torch suitable for morse signalling.

19.3   Radar Reflector

Every ship should carry a radar reflector complying with the Department of Transport Marine Radar Reflector Performance Specification 1977.

19.4   Measuring Instruments

Every ship should carry a barometer and an anemometer. Ships of 15 metres in length and over should be fitted with an inclinometer.

19.5   Wire Cutting Equipment

Every ship should carry wire cutting equipment for use in the event of dismasting.

20 Anchors and Cables

Every ship should be provided with at least two anchors and
cables in accordance with the following table of minimum
sizes.

The requirements shown in the table are for ships of normal
sailing yacht form. Where such ships have an unusually high
windage, such as heavy rigging, viz. square-rigger, or large
superstructures, the weight of each anchor should be
increased by 25%. The diameter of the anchor cable should
be appropriate to the weight of the increased size of anchor.

The anchor sizes given in the table are for high holding
power (HHP) types i.e. spade, plough, etc. If a fisherman
type of anchor is to be provided, the weight from the table
should be increased by 25% but the diameter of the anchor
cable need not be increased.

The length of each anchor cable should be appropriate to the
operating area but in any event should not be less than 55
metres for both the main and kedge anchors. The anchor
cable for the main anchor for ships of 15 metres and above
should be of chain; the cable for main anchors for ships
below 15 metres and for kedge anchors may be of chain or
rope. Where the anchor cable is of rope, there should be at
least 5 metres of chain between the rope and the anchor.

The ship should be provided with a towline of not less than
the length and diameter of the kedge anchor cable. The
towline may be the warp for the kedge anchor.

Where an anchor weighs more than 30 kg, a windlass should
be provided for working the anchor.

There should be a strong securing point on the foredeck and
a fairlead or roller at the stem head which can be closed over
the cable.

Length	Anchor Weight		Anchor Cable Diameter			
Overall	Main	Kedge	Main		Kedge	
			Chain	Rope	Chain	Rope
(metres)	(kg)	(kg)	(mm)	(mm)	(mm)	(mm)
Up to 9	15	8	8	12	6	10
10	17	9	8	14	8	12
11	20	10	8	14	8	12
12	23	12	8	14	8	12
13	26	13	9.5	16	8	12
14	30	15	9.5	16	8	14
15	34	17	9.5	–	8	14
16	38	19	11	–	8	14
17	44	22	11	–	8	14
18	50	25	11	–	9.5	16
19	56	28	12.5	–	9.5	16
20	62	31	12.5	–	9.5	16
21	69	35	12.5	–	11	16
22	76	38	12.5	–	11	16
23	83	42	14	–	11	16
24	90	45	14	–	11	16

Notes
1. Chain Cable diameter given is for short link. Where stud link cable is to be used, the diameter may be modified in accordance with the breaking load.

2. The rope diameter given is for nylon. Where other fibres are to be used, the diameter should be modified in accordance with the breaking load.

3. Where the anchors and cables are manufactured to imperial sizes, the metric equivalent of the anchor weight and the cable diameter should not be less than 10% below the table value.

4. Where a heavier kedge anchor is provided, the weight of the main anchor may be reduced provided the combined weight of both anchors is not less than 160% of the table main anchor weight.

21   Accommodation

When a sail training ship is intended to be at sea for more than 24 hours then it will be necessary to provide an adequate standard of accommodation for all on board. In considering such accommodation, primary concern should be directed towards ensuring the health and safety aspects of the personnel e.g. the ventilation, lighting, heating, water services, galley services and the access/escape arrangements. In particular the following standards should be observed:

21.1   Ventilation

Effective means of ventilation should be provided to all enclosed spaces which are for use by the personnel on board. Moreover, mechanical ventilation should be provided to accommodation spaces which are situated completely below the level of the Weather Deck (excluding any coach roof) on those ships intended to make long international voyages or operate in tropical waters and which carry more than 8 berthed persons below deck. Such ventilation arrangements should be capable of providing at least 6 changes of air per hour when the access openings to the spaces are closed.

21.2   Lighting

An electric lighting system should be installed which is capable of supplying adequate light to all enclosed accommodation and working spaces. The system should be designed and installed in a manner which will minimise the risk of fire and electric shock.

21.3   Water Services

An adequate supply of fresh drinking water should be provided and piped to convenient positions throughout the accommodation spaces. In addition an emergency supply of drinking water should be carried at the rate of 2 litres per person.

21.4   Sleeping Accommodation

A bunk or cot should be provided for every person on board and at least 50% of these should be fitted with lee boards or lee cloths.

21.5   Galley

The galley should be fitted with a cooking stove and a sink and have adequate working surface for the preparation of food when underway in a seaway. If the stove is gimballed it should be protected by a crash bar or other means to prevent it being tilted when it is free to swing. A strap, portable bar or other means should be provided to allow the cook to secure himself in position, with both hands free for working, when the ship is heeled on either tack. There should be secure stowage for food in the vicinity of the galley.

21.6   Toilet Facilities

Adequate toilet facilities separated from the rest of the accommodation should be provided for all on board. In general there should be at least one marine type flushing water closet and one wash hand basin for every 12 persons.

21.7   Securement of Heavy Equipment

All heavy items of equipment such as ballast, batteries, cooking stove, etc., should be securely fastened in place in case of inversion.

All stowage lockers containing heavy items should have lids or doors with secure fastening.

21.8   Hand Holds and Grab-Rails

There should be sufficient hand holds and grab-rails within the accommodation to allow safe movement around the accommodation when underway in a seaway.

21.9   Stowage Facilities for Personal Effects

Adequate stowage facilities for clothing and personal effects should be provided for every person on board.

22   Protection of Personnel

22.1   Deckhouses

Every deckhouse used for accommodation of personnel should be of efficient construction.

22.2   Bulwarks and Guard rails

The perimeters of exposed decks should be fitted with
bulwarks, guard rails or guard wires of sufficient strength and
height. In general, taut double guardrails with the upper rail
or wire at a height of not less than 600 mm (24″) above the
deck should be fitted around the working deck. They should
be supported at intervals not exceeding 2.2. metres (7′–3″). If
the cockpit opens aft to the sea, additional guardrails should
be fitted so that there is no vertical opening greater than 500
mm (20″). There should be a fixed bow pulpit forward of the
headstay of at least the same height as the guardrails except
in way of a substantial bowsprit.

22.3   Safety Harnesses

Every ship should carry a safety harness for each person on
board.

22.4   Safety Harness Securing Points

Efficient means for securing the life lines of safety harnesses
should be provided on exposed decks, with grabrails on the
sides and ends of deck houses. Access stairways, ladderways
and corridors should be provided with handrails. Fastening
points for the attachment of safety harness life lines should
be arranged having regard to the likely need for work on or
above deck. In general, securing points should be provided in
the following positions:
  (a) close to the companionway;
  (b) on both sides of the cockpit.
In addition jackstays, secured to strong points, should be
provided on each side of the ship to enable crew members to
traverse the length of the weather deck.

22.5   Toe Rails

A toe rail of not less than 25 mm (1″) in height should be
fitted around the working deck.

22.6   The Surface of Working Decks

The surface of the working deck should be non-slip.
Acceptable surfaces are: unpainted wood; a non-skid pattern

moulded into GRP; non-slip deck paint; or an efficient nonslip covering. Particular attention should be paid to hatch covers where these are fitted on the working deck and to sloping coachroof sides where these effectively constitute a working deck when the ship is heeled.

22.7 Boarding Ladder or Scrambling Net

An overside boarding ladder or scrambling net should be provided which extends from the Weather Deck to at least 600 mm (24") below the operational waterline.

23 Medical Stores

All ships should carry medical stores prescribed in the Merchant Shipping (Medical Stores) Regulations 1986 (as amended) except that:

(a) ships carrying more than eight persons within the Limited European Trading Area or on voyages not exceeding 100 miles elsewhere in the world may carry the restricted list of stores (revised Scale II) at Annex 14; and

(b) ships carrying not more than eight persons on voyages not exceeding 72 hours duration between ports in the United Kingdom and ports on the continent of Europe between Brest and the River Elbe may carry the list of stores (Scale IV) at Annex 15.

24 Tenders/Dinghies

Every ship should carry one or more rigid or inflatable tenders. Every tender should be clearly marked with the number of people of mass 75 kg that it can safely carry and with the name of the parent ship. Inflatable tenders should be regularly inspected by the operator and maintained in a safe condition.

25 Storm Sails

All ships should carry efficient storm sails capable of taking the ship to windward in heavy weather.

26 Manning

Every ship should be safely manned. The qualification of the master (and of the other deck officers where applicable) for operations in various areas is the subject of a General Exemption. The conditions applicable to the General Exemption and the responsibility of the owner for the safe manning of the ship are detailed in Annex 7.

27 Surveys, Certification, Inspection and Maintenance

27.1   Any ship used as a sail training ship on or after 1 January 1991 should comply with the appropriate requirements of this Code and have a Sail Training Ship Certificate issued by a Sail Training Ship Certifying Authority in accordance with Sections 27.3 or 27.4.

In the case of an existing sail training ship which has a current load line or load line exemption certificate, the ship can continue to operate on the basis of existing certification until the expiry of the current certificate. Alternatively, or when that certificate expires, the owner or managing agent may choose between renewing the load line or load line exemption certificate in accordance with the previous arrangements or, preferably, apply to one of the Sail Training Ship Certifying Authorities for the issue of a Sail Training Ship Certificate in accordance with the requirements of Sections 27.3.2, 27.4.2.3 or 27.4.3.3 of the Code, as appropriate.

Sail Training Ships surveyed, certificated, maintained and periodically inspected in accordance with the requirements of this Code will be the subject of a General Exemption from the relevant requirements of the appropriate Merchant Shipping Rules and Regulations. The Certifying Authority may inspect a ship at any time during the period of validity of a certificate.

For the purposes of this section:-

"Survey" means a full and detailed examination of the ship, its machinery and equipment to ascertain whether they comply with the requirements of the Code. At least part of the survey should be conducted whilst the ship is out of the water; and

"Inspection" means a general examination of the ship, its machinery and equipment as far as can be seen in order to ascertain whether they are still in seaworthy condition. The thoroughness of the inspection will depend upon the condition of the ship and its equipment.

27.2 Maintaining and Operating the Ship

It is the responsibility of the owner or his contracted agent to ensure that the ship is properly maintained and operated in accordance with any conditions stated on the Sail Training Ship Certificate. This, in effect, means that he should examine the ship, its machinery and equipment at regular intervals and arrange for the required inspections or surveys to be undertaken by the due date.

The agreement of the Sail Training Ship Certifying Authority should be obtained before any major repairs are made.

27.3 Surveys and inspections of ships of 15 metres in length and over or carrying 15 or more persons

27.3.1 *New Sail Training Ships*

(a) Before a Sail Training Ship Certificate can be issued it will be necessary for the ship to be surveyed by an authorised surveyor to establish that it complies with the appropriate requirements of the Code.

(b) When the surveyor is satisfied that the ship meets the appropriate requirements of the Code he should complete, in duplicate, a Declaration of Survey of a Sail Training Ship, the form of which is shown at Annex 8. The surveyor should indicate on the form the maximum period for which he recommends that the Sail Training Ship Certificate should be valid. The maximum period should not exceed 5 years. Any operating conditions, for example, geographical operating limits, should be shown on the declaration. The declaration on completion of survey should then be sent to the owner or his agent for onward transmission to the appropriate Sail Training Ship Certifying Authority.

(c) On receipt of the completed declaration the Sail Training Ship Certifying Authority, when it is satisfied that it is proper to do so, will issue to the owner or his agent, in duplicate, a Sail Training Ship Certificate, the form of which is shown at Annex 9. One of these certificates should be retained on board the ship.

(d) For the certificate to remain valid for the period indicated it will be necessary for the ship to be inspected annually by an authorised surveyor to establish that it continues to comply with the appropriate requirements of the Code and any conditions shown on the certificate. The inspections should take place not more than 3 months before nor 3 months later than the anniversary date of the issue of the certificate. The time and place of such inspections should be recorded on the certificate in the space provided.

(e) On expiry of the certificate a survey for renewal of the certificate should be carried out in the same manner as the initial survey.

27.3.2 *Existing Sail Training Ships*

(a) These ships should be surveyed in accordance with the procedures given for new ships in Section 27.3.1.

(b) The Sail Training Ship Certifying Authority will issue duplicate copies of the Sail Training Ship Certificate under the same provisions as those described for new ships in Section 27.3.1.

(c) The initial survey and issue of certificates should be carried out according to the age of the ship as follows:

  (i) Ships built before 1 January 1978 should be surveyed and issued with a Sail Training Ship Certificate not later than 31 March 1991;

  (ii) all other ships should be surveyed and issued with a Sail Training Ship Certificate not later than 31 March 1992.

27.4 Surveys and inspections of ships less than 15 metres in length and carrying fewer than 15 persons

27.4.1 *General*

(a) The owner or managing agent should forward to the Sail Training Ship Certifying Authority details of the ship including principal dimensions of hull and rig, name of builder and designer, year of build, class (if any) and sufficient information for the Certifying Authority to allocate a stability category in accordance with Section 11.1.2 of the Code.

(b) The Sail Training Ship Certifying Authority will then decide whether or not the ship is of a suitable type and will inform the owner or managing agent of the surveys and inspections required in accordance with the following paragraphs.

27.4.2   Ships built of FRP/GRP

27.4.2.1   *New Sail Training Ships (as defined) of new construction*

(a) Prior to entering service as a sail training ship, the owner or managing agent should submit to the Sail Training Ship Certifying Authority a Builder's Declaration, the form of which is shown at Annex 11, that the hull structure, fittings and equipment installed by the Builder are in compliance with the requirements of the Code, and also a declaration by the owner or managing agent, the form of which is shown at Annex 12, that the equipment and fittings not covered by the Builder's Declaration are in compliance with the requirements of the Code.

(b) The Builder's Declaration in respect of hull structure may be replaced by a certificate of hull construction issued by one of the Classification Societies listed in Section 4.2.1(a).

(c) On receipt of the above information the Certifying Authority, when it is satisfied that it is proper to do so, will issue to the owner or his agent, in duplicate, a Sail Training Ship Certificate. One of these certificates should be retained on board the ship.

(d) For the certificate to remain valid for the period indicated the ship should be inspected annually by a person appointed by the Certifying Authority to establish that it continues to comply with the appropriate requirements of the Code and any conditions shown on the certificate. The inspection should take place not more than 3 months before nor 3 months later than the anniversary date of the issue of the certificate.

(e) As an alternative to the procedure described in sub-paragraph (d) the owner may complete an Inspection

Questionnaire, the form of which is shown at Annex 10. The Inspection Questionnaire should be completed within the time scale above and sent to the Certifying Authority who will examine it for confirmation of compliance with the appropriate section of the Code.

(f) During the period of validity of the certificate the ship may be subject to a random inspection by a person appointed by the Certifying Authority.

(g) The period of validity of the certificate will be determined by the age of the ship, the survey conducted by an authorised surveyor and any recommendations he may make. In general the ship is to be surveyed as follows:

(i) not less than 12 months or more than 2 years after the date of issue of the first certificate;

(ii) at intervals not exceeding 4 years when the ship is more than 10 years but less than 20 years old;

(iii) at intervals not exceeding 2 years when the ship is more than 20 years old.

(h) In addition to these surveys the ship may be surveyed at any time by the Certifying Authority or following repairs or modifications of a significant nature.

27.4.2.2 *New Sail Training Ships (as defined) which are not of new construction*

(a) Prior to entering service as a sail training ship, the ship should be surveyed by an authorised surveyor to establish that it complies with the appropriate sections of the Code. When the surveyor is satisfied that this is the case he is to complete in duplicate a Declaration of Survey of a Sail Training Ship. The declaration should be sent to the owner or his managing agent for onward transmission to the Certifying Authority.

(b) On receipt of the declaration the Certifying Authority, when it is satisfied that it is proper to do so, will issue to the owner or his agent, in duplicate, a Sail Training Ship Certificate. One of these certificates should be retained on board the ship.

(c) In order for the certificate to remain valid the ship should be inspected annually or an Inspection Questionnaire completed as described in sub section 27.4.2.1 above.

(d) The period of validity of the certificate will be determined by the age of the ship, the survey conducted by an authorised surveyor and any recommendations he may make. These surveys should be carried out as follows:

(i) at intervals not exceeding 4 years when the ship is more than 10 years but less than 20 years old;

(ii) at intervals not exceeding 2 years when the ship is more than 20 years old.

(e) In addition to these surveys the ship may be surveyed at any time required by the Certifying Authority or following repairs of a significant nature.

27.4.2.3 *Existing Sail Training Ships*

These ships should be dealt with in the same way as new sail training ships not of new construction as described in sub section 27.4.2.2 except that the initial survey should be carried out not later than 1 January 1993. Prior to the date of the initial survey, the Certifying Authority may issue a short term certificate signifying compliance with the Code if it is satisfied that it may properly do so having regard to the knowledge that the Authority has of the ship including its condition and the area of operation.

27.4.3 *Ships built of other materials*

27.4.3.1 *New sail training ships (as defined) of new construction*

(a) Prior to entering service as a sail training ship the owner or managing agent should submit to the Sail Training Ship Certifying Authority a Builder's Declaration, the form of which is shown in Annex 11, that the hull structure, fittings and equipment installed by the Builder are in compliance with the requirements of the Code. In addition, a declaration by the owner or managing agent, the form of which is shown in Annex 12, should be submitted to indicate that the equipment and fittings not covered by the Builder's Declaration are in compliance with the requirements of the Code.

(b) The Builder's Declaration in respect of hull structure may be replaced by a certificate of hull construction issued by one of the Classification Societies listed in Section 4.2.1(a).

(c) On receipt of the above information the Certifying Authority, when it is satisfied that it is proper to do so, will issue to the owner or his agent, in duplicate, a Sail Training Ship Certificate. One of these certificates should be retained on board the ship.

(d) For the certificate to remain valid the ship should be inspected annually by a person appointed by the Certifying Authority to establish that it continues to comply with the appropriate requirements of the Code and any conditions shown on the certificate. The inspection should take place not more than 3 months before nor 3 months later than the anniversary date of the issue of the certificate.

(e) As an alternative to the procedure described in sub-paragraph (d) the owner may complete an Inspection Questionnaire, the form of which is shown at Annex 10. The Inspection Questionnaire should be completed within the time scale above and sent to the Certifying Authority who will examine it for confirmation of compliance with the appropriate section of the Code.

(f) During the period of validity of the certificate the ship may be subject to a random inspection by a person appointed by the Certifying Authority.

(g) The period of validity of the certificate will be determined by the age of the ship, the survey conducted by an authorised surveyor and any recommendations he may make. In general the ship is to be surveyed as follows:

(i) not less than 12 months or more than 2 years after the date of issue of the first certificate;

(ii) at intervals not exceeding 4 years when the ship is more than 5 years but less than 15 years old;

(iii) at intervals not exceeding 2 years when the ship is more than 15 years old.

(h) In addition to these surveys the ship may be surveyed at any time required by the Certifying Authority or following repairs or modifications of a significant nature.

27.4.3.2 *New Sail Training Ships (as defined) which are not of new construction*

(a) Prior to entering service as a sail training ship the ship should be surveyed by an authorised surveyor to establish that it complies with the appropriate sections of the Code. When the surveyor is satisfied that this is the case he will complete in duplicate a Declaration of Survey of a Sail Training Ship. The declaration should be sent to the owner or his managing agent for onward transmission to the Certifying Authority.

(b) On receipt of the declaration the Certifying Authority, when it is satisfied that it is proper to do so, will issue to the owner or his agent, in duplicate, a Sail Training Ship Certificate. One of these certificates should be retained on board the ship.

(c) In order for the certificate to remain valid the ship should be inspected annually or an Inspection Questionnaire completed as described in sub section 27.4.3.1 above.

(d) the period of validity of the certificate will be determined by the age of the ship, the survey conducted by an authorised surveyor and any recommendations he may make. These surveys should be carried out as follows:

(i) at intervals not exceeding 4 years when the ship is more than 5 years but less than 15 years old;

(ii) at intervals not exceeding 2 years when the ship is more than 15 years old.

(e) In addition to these surveys the ship may be surveyed at any time required by the Certifying Authority or following repairs of a significant nature.

27.4.3.3   *Existing Sail Training Ships*

These ships should be dealt with in the same way as new sail training ships not of new construction as described in sub section 27.4.3.2 except that the initial survey should be carried out not later than 1 January 1993. Prior to the date of the initial survey, the Certifying Authority may issue a short term certificate signifying compliance with the Code if it is satisfied that it may properly do so having regard to the knowledge that the Authority has of the ship including its condition and the area of operation.

ANNEX 1

LIFE-SAVING APPLIANCES

Equipment	*Ships under 24 metres in length*	
	Fewer than 15 persons	15 persons or more
Liferafts	Note (a)	Note (a)
Portable two-way radio-telephone sets	1 – Note (b)	1 – Note (b)
Radar transponders	1 – Note (c)	1 – Note (c)
Lifebuoys	2 – Note (d)	4 – Note (d)
Buoyant lifeline	1 × 18 metres	1 × 18 metres
Lifejackets	Note (e)	Note (e)
Rocket parachute flares	4	4
Red hand flares	6	6
Buoyant smoke signals	2	2
General emergency alarm signal	–	Yes
Training manual	1	2
Instructions for on-board maintenance	Yes	Yes
Life-Saving Signals and Rescue Signal Table (SOLAS No. 1)	1	1

Notes

(a) Liferafts should be provided of such number and capacity that in the event of any one liferaft being lost or rendered unserviceable there is sufficient capacity remaining for all on board. Ships carrying fewer than 15 persons and operating solely within the Limited European Area or within the Mediterranean and Black Seas should be provided with liferaft capacity to accommodate at least the total number of persons on board. Liferafts should comply with the Merchant Shipping (Life-Saving Appliances) Regulations 1986, or with [ISO/DP 9650 – Inflatable Liferafts for Recreational Craft]*

---

*This draft proposal has yet to be finalised and printed as a BRITISH and ISO standard.

Liferafts on ships carrying 15 or more persons should be stowed on or near the centreline of the ship where they can be readily launched on either side. They should be stowed on the upper deck or in an open space and should be fitted with float free arrangements so that the liferaft floats free and inflates automatically when the ship sinks. Such liferafts should be stowed in GRP containers.

In ships carrying fewer than 15 persons liferafts may be stowed in dedicated lockers opening directly onto the upper deck.

(b) Ships provided with a 406 MHz EPIRB need not be provided with a portable two-way radiotelephone set.

(c) Ships not provided with a 406 MHz EPIRB need not be provided with a radar transponder.

(d) For ships carrying fewer than 15 persons the lifebuoys may be of the horseshoe type. On all ships two lifebuoys should be provided with a drogue and a self-igniting light. One of these lifebuoys should also be provided with a dan buoy with a marker flag so placed that it will be at a height of 2 metres above sea level in calm conditions.

On ships carrying 15 or more persons the other two lifebuoys should be fitted with buoyant lifelines at least 18 metres in length.

(e) One lifejacket should be provided for each person plus spare lifejackets for 10% of the ship's complement or two lifejackets, whichever is the greater. Lifejackets should be Department of Transport approved or comply with British Standard 3595: 1981. Lifejackets should be provided with a whistle, light and retro-reflective material.

ANNEX 2

FIRE FIGHTING EQUIPMENT FOR SHIPS OF LESS THAN 24 METRES IN LENGTH

LESS THAN 15 METRES IN LENGTH AND FEWER THAN 15 PERSONS (1)	LESS THAN 24 METRES IN LENGTH (OTHER THAN COL. 1) (2)
One hand powered fire pump (outside engine space) or one power driven fire pump (outside engine space),* with sea and hose connections, capable of delivering one jet of water to any part of the ship through hose and nozzle. One fire hose of adequate length with 10mm nozzle and suitable spray nozzle; or One multi-purpose fire extinguisher to BS 5423 with minimum fire rating of 13A/113B (in addition to that required below). Fixed fire extinguishing in engine space which may consist of a portable fire extinguisher arranged to discharge into the space. Not less than one multi-purpose fire extinguisher to BS 5423 with minimum fire rating of 5A/34B provided at each exit from accommodation spaces to the open deck. In no case shall there be less than two such extinguishers provided. At least two fire buckets with lanyards. Buckets may be of metal, plastic or canvas and shall be suitable for their intended service. One fire blanket in galley or cooking area (BS 6575 – light duty type).	One hand powered fire pump (outside engine space) or one power driven fire pump (outside engine space)*, with sea and hose connections, capable of delivering one jet of water to any part of the ship through hose and nozzle. One fire hose of adequate length with 10mm nozzle and suitable spray nozzle. Fixed fire extinguishing in engine space which may consist of a portable extinguisher arranged to discharge into the space. Not less than two multi-purpose fire extinguishers to BS 5423 with a minimum fire rating of 13A/144B At least two fire buckets with lanyards. Buckets may be of metal, plastic or canvas and shall be suitable for their intended service. One fire blanket in galley or cooking area (BS 6575 – light duty type).

* This may be one of the bilge pumps required by Section 10 when fitted with suitable change over arrangements which are readily accessible.

ANNEX 3

STRUCTURAL FIRE PROTECTION

FIGURE 6

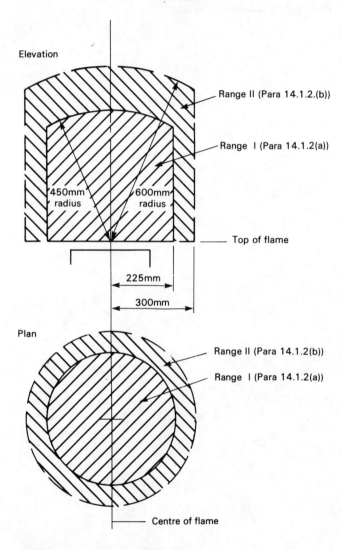

Distances from an open flame used for special requirements for materials including surface finishes (see paragraph 14.1.2).

DEPARTMENT OF TRADE   MERCHANT SHIPPING
NOTICE NO. M. 984

USE OF LIQUEFIED PETROLEUM GAS (LPG) IN DOMESTIC INSTALLATIONS AND APPLIANCES ON SHIPS, FISHING VESSELS, BARGES, LAUNCHES, AND PLEASURE CRAFT

EXPLOSIONS, FIRES AND ACCIDENTS RESULTING FROM LEAKAGE OF GAS

Notice to Shipbuilders, Owners, Masters, Skippers, Officers and Seamen of Merchant Ships and Fishing Vessels, Owners and Builders of pleasure craft and to other users of marine craft

This notice supersedes Notice No. M603

In view of the considerable use on smaller cargo ships, fishing vessels, tugs, barges, launches and pleasure craft of bottled hydrocarbon gases for cooking, water and space heating, refrigerators, etc., the Department wishes to draw attention to the possible dangers which may accompany their use and to the need for installations to comply at least with the requirements of British Standard Institution publication BS 5482: Part 3: 1979 – The code of practice for domestic butane and propane gas-burning installations; Part 3 – Installations in boats, yachts and other vessels. Individual appliances and fittings should comply with the relevant British Standard Specifications listed in BS 5482: Part 3: 1979, some of which are given at Appendix 1.

2. The possible dangers associated with the misuse of such installations include fire, explosion and asphyxiation due to the leakage of gas from appliances, storage containers or defective fittings or due to an accumulation of gas following flame failure. Incidents may result in loss of life and sometimes cause serious material damage. The siting of gas consuming appliances and storage containers and the provision of adequate ventilation of the spaces containing them are **consequently most important.**

3. In addition to the risk of asphyxiation should the leakage or accumulation of gas occur in an enclosed space, there is also the risk of carbon monoxide poisoning when the

appliance is in use. It is dangerous to sleep in spaces where gas-consuming open-flame appliances are left burning and it follows that heaters without flues should not be sited in areas designed as sleeping quarters or in unventilated spaces communicating directly with such areas.

4. Furthermore, open-flame heaters and gas refrigerators with non-enclosed burners may present a serious hazard from the fire and explosion aspects and, if possible, their use should be avoided.

5. In the United Kingdom the gases most commonly used for domestic Liquified Petroleum Gas (LPG) installations in ships are butane and propane conforming to BS 4250 – Commercial butane and propane. A stenching agent is added to enable the presence of gas to be detected by smell even when its concentration in air is below its lower limit of flammability. Trade names and the suppliers of some of these gases are given in Appendix 3.

6. It is important to remember with LPG installations that the gases, although heavier than air, if released, may travel some distance tending to fall to the bottom of a compartment. Here they diffuse and may form an explosive mixture with air, as in the case of petrol vapours.

7. A frequent cause of incidents involving LPG Installations is the use of unsuitable fittings or the replacement of items such as flexible hoses with temporary rubber or plastic tubing. It is essential that any repair or replacement part is in accordance with the original specification of the equipment as detailed in BS 5482: Part 3: 1979.

8. In view of the elements of danger in the use of LPG installations a warning notice in red should be displayed adjacent to each appliance to read as follows:

WARNING

1. **DO NOT LIGHT IF LEAKAGE IS SUSPECTED.**
2. **BEWARE OF ANY UNUSUAL SMELL AS THIS MAY INDICATE LEAKAGE FROM THE APPLIANCE.**
3. **DO NOT CHECK FOR LEAKS WITH A NAKED FLAME**
4. **MAINTAIN GOOD VENTILATION AT ALL TIMES.**

9. In conjunction with any LPG Installation the provision of an automatic gas detection and alarm system of a reliable type is strongly recommended and is absolutely necessary when a cooking or other gas-consuming appliance is fitted in sleeping or other spaces below decks. It is essential that any electrical equipment associated with the gas detection and alarm system should be certified as being flame-proof or intrinsically safe for the gas being used.

10. As expressed above LPG installations should at least comply with the requirements of BS 5482: Part 3: 1979 but the Department also wishes to stress the importance of obtaining expert advice regarding the fitting of LPG Installations and of the need to ensure that such installations and associated alarm systems receive adequate (and expert) maintenance in service.

11. BS 5482: Part 3: 1979 deals very fully with all aspects of LPG Installations but some general comments are made in Appendix 2 as all users of such installations may not have access to this publication or to the selection of individual specifications listed in Appendix 1.

12. LPG Installations in mechanically propelled sea-going fishing vessels registered in the United Kingdom need to comply, as appropriate, with the requirements of Rules 34 and 61 of the Fishing Vessels (Safety Provisions) Rules 1975. However the warnings detailed above are applicable to all fishing vessels and such installations not directly covered by the Fishing Vessels Rules should be in accordance with the recommendations of this Notice.

13. Attention is also drawn to the requirements of Regulation 6(6) of the Merchant Shipping (Crew Accommodation) Regulations 1978.

Department of Trade
Marine Division
London WC1V 6LP

August 1981

APPENDIX 1

SELECTION OF RELEVANT BRITISH STANDARD SPECIFICATIONS

BS 2491   Domestic cooking appliances for use with liquefied petroleum gases.

BS 2773   Domestic single room space heating appliances for use with liquified petroleum gases.

BS 2871   Copper and copper alloys. Tubes.
Part 1. Copper tubes for water, gas and sanitation.
Part 2. Tubes for general purposes.

BS 2883   Domestic instantaneous and storage water heaters for use with liquefied petroleum gases.

BS 3016   Pressure regulators and automatic change over devices for use with liquified petroleum gases.

BS 3212   Flexible rubber tubing and hose (including connections where fitted and safety recommendations) for use in LPG vapour phase and LPG/air installations.

BS 3605   Seamless and welded austenitic stainless steel pipes and tubes for pressure purposes.

BS 4104   Catering equipment burning liquefied petroleum gases.

BS 4368   Carbon and stainless steel compression couplings for tubes.
Part 1. Heavy series.
Part 3. Light series (metric).

BS 5045   Transportable gas containers.
Part 2. Steel containers up to 130 litres water capacity with welded seams.

BS 5314   Specification for gas heater catering equipment.

BS 5386   Specification for gas heating appliances.
Part 1. Gas burning appliances for instantaneous production of hot water for deomestic use.

APPENDIX 2

GENERAL COMMENTS ON LPG INSTALLATIONS

1. Stowage of gas containers

Wherever possible gas containers should be stowed on the open deck or in a well-ventilated compartment on deck so that any gas which may leak can disperse rapidly. Where deck stowage is impracticable and the containers have to be stowed in a compartment below deck, such a space should be adequately ventilated to a safe place and any electrical equipment in the space should be of flame-proof construction. In all cases stowage should be such that the containers are positively restrained against movement, preferably in secure mountings specially designed for the purpose. On multiple container installations a non-return valve should be placed in the supply line near to the stop valve on each container. If a change-over device is used it must be provided with non-return valves to isolate any depleted container. Where more than one container can supply a system it should not be put into use with a container removed. Where stowage below deck or use of appliances in accommodation is unavoidable, an added precaution is the provision of remote closure of the main gas supply from the containers. Containers not in use or not being fitted into an installation should always have the protecting cap in place over the container valve. Containers should never be lifted by means of a rope around the valve.

2. Stowage of spare and empty gas containers

It is important that the stowage of spare and empty gas containers receive the same consideration as the positioning of operating containers, particularly with regard to ventilation and electrical equipment should the spare containers be stowed below decks.

3. Automatic Safety Gas Cut-off Devices

A device should be fitted in the supply pipe from the gas container to the consuming appliances which will shut off the gas automatically in the event of loss of pressure in the supply line, eg, should a connecting pipe fracture. The device should be of a type which requires deliberate manual operation to re-set it to restore the gas supply. It is strongly recommended that all gas consuming devices should be fitted, where practicable, with an automatic shut-off device which operates in the event of flame failure.

4. Open-flame heaters and gas refrigerators

When such appliances are installed, they should be well secured so as to avoid movement and be preferably of a type where the gas flames are isolated in a totally enclosed shield, arranged in such a way that the air supply and combustion gas outlets are piped to the open air. However, in the case of refrigerators where the burners are fitted with flame arrestor gauzes, shielding of the gas flame may be an optional feature. Refrigerators should be fitted with a flame failure device and flueless heaters should be selected only if fitted with atmosphere-sensitive cut-off devices to shut-off the gas supply at a CO_2 concentration of not more than 1.5 per cent by volume. Heaters of the catalytic type should not be used.

5. Fittings and Pipework

Solid drawn copper alloy fittings or stainless steel tube with appropriate compression or screwed fittings are recommended for general use for pipework for LPG installations. Aluminium or steel tubing and any materials having a low melting point such as rubber or plastic should not be used. Lengths of flexible piping (if required for flexible connections) should be kept as short as possible, be protected from inadvertent damage and comply with the appropriate British Standard.

6. Ventilating Arrangements

(a) It is highly desirable that compartments containing a gas-consuming appliance should not have access doors or openings direct to accommodation spaces or their passage-ways, but where this is impracticable it is advisable that mechanical exhaust ventilation trunked to within 12 in of the floor adjacent to the appliances and adequate inlet ventilation be provided.

(b) Compartments containing a gas-consuming appliance which are situated upon an open deck with direct access to the adjacent deck and with no opening direct to accommodation spaces or their passageways should be adequately ventilated, preferably by mechanical means.

(c) In pleasure craft and in some small ships where it may be impracticable to provide the mechanical ventilation referred to in sub-paragraphs (a) and (b) above, all compartments where gas-consuming devices are used should have adequate natural ventilation of a type which cannot readily be closed and which will prevent a dangerous accumulation of gas. The ventilation should provide for extraction of any gas which might leak from the system, as well as providing a fresh air supply. Since the gas, which is heavier than air, tends to fall to the lowest level, exhaust ventilation openings should be led from a position low in the space. Such ventilation might be provided by wind-actuated self-trimming cowls or rotary exhauster heads.

(d) When mechanical ventilation is fitted to any space in which gas containers or gas-consuming appliances are situated, such materials and design should be such as will eliminate incentive sparking due to friction or impact of the fan impeller with its casing. Electric motors driving fans should be situated outside the space and also, whenever practicable, outside the ventilation trunking and clear of outlets, but suitably certified flame-proof motors should be used if this cannot be achieved. Ventilator outlets should be in a safe area free from ignition hazard. Ventilation systems serving spaces containing storage containers or gas-consuming appliances should be separate from any other ventilation system. Mechanical exhaust ventilation trunking should be led down to the lower part of the space adjacent to the appliance.

(e) Notwithstanding (b) above, Regulation 32(11) of Part 1 of the Merchant Shipping (Crew Accommodation) Regulation 1978 requires mechanical exhaust ventilation to be provided for galleys in any ship over 1,000 tons gross and Regulation 25(9) of Schedule 6 to the same Regulations (existing ships) requires mechanical exhaust ventilation in any galley.

(f) In cases where loss of life has occurred due to asphyxiation or carbon monoxide poisoning the ventilation system has been found to be deficient because ventilators have been interfered with or neglected. It is not unusual to find ventilators deliberately blocked, and butterfly and sliding ventilators have been found to be in the closed position and immovable. The importance of adequate ventilation of spaces containing gas consuming appliances cannot be too strongly emphasised and on no account must a ventilation system be interfered with so as to prevent it functioning correctly.

(g) Whilst adequate ventilation is a prerequisite for safety, consideration should be given to the siting of gas-consuming appliances in relation to the ventilating system such that air turbulence does not bring about the extinction of unshielded gas flames and thus permit the escape of gas.

7. Gas Detection

Suitable means of detecting the leakage of gas should preferably be provided in each compartment containing a gas-consuming appliance and where this is a detector, it should generally be securely fixed in the lower part of the compartment in the vicinity of the gas-consuming appliance. Any gas detector should preferably be of a type which will be actuated promptly and automatically by the presence of a gas concentration in air not greater than 0.5 per cent (representing approximately 25 per cent of the lower explosive limit) and should incorporate an audible and a visible alarm, although on small craft a portable manually operated detector may be used. Where electrical detection equipment is fitted it is essential that it should be certified as being flame-proof or intrinsically safe for the gas being used. In all cases where detection and alarm equipment are used, the alarm unit and indicating panel should be situated outside the space containing the gas storage and consuming appliances.

Similar provision for automatic gas detection and alarm should also be made in small vessels, such as pleasure craft and barges, if a cooking or other gas-consuming appliance is fitted in sleeping or messing spaces below deck.

Detectors can be rendered unsafe for use in explosive atmospheres by inexpert servicing, particularly in respect of arrangements for sealing off the detection chamber. Any maintenance should therefore be carried out by persons competent to do so or by replacement of the detection unit.

In all cases the arrangements should be such that detection devices can be tested frequently whilst the craft is in service.

8. Emergency Action

A suitable notice detailing action to be taken when an alarm is given by the gas detection system should be displayed on board the craft. In addition, the information given should include the following:

(a) the need to be always alert for gas leakage;

(b) when leakage is suspected all gas-consuming appliances should be shut off at the main supply from the container and no smoking should be permitted until it is safe to do so. **NAKED LIGHTS SHOULD NEVER BE USED AS A MEAN OF LOCATING LEAKS:**

(c) the correct use and maintenance of fire extinguishing appliances of which an adequate number should always be carried;

(d) the need for users to be fully aware of the contents of the consumer instructions and emergency procedures issued in accordance with clause 22 of BS 5482: Part 3: 1979.

APPENDIX 3

SUPPLIERS OF LPG USED IN THE SHIPPING INDUSTRY

Supplier	Gas
1. Propane	
Air Products Ltd	Propane
British Oxygen Co. Ltd	Propane
BP Oil Ltd	BP Gas – Propane
Calor Gas Ltd	Calor Propane
Calor Kosangas (Northern Ireland) Ltd	Propane
Shell UK Oil	Propagas
2. Butane	
BP Oil Ltd	BP Gas – Butane
Calor Gas Ltd	Calor Gas
Calor Kosangas (Northern Ireland) Ltd	Butane
Shell UK Oil	Butagas

DEPARTMENT OF TRANSPORT   MERCHANT SHIPPING
NOTICE NO. M. 1194

THE STATUS OF PERSONS CARRIED ON UNITED
KINGDOM SHIPS

This Notice is addressed to Shipowners, Charterers, Masters and Persons in charge of United Kingdom Ships

1.   During an appeal case** heard in the High Court in 1983, the legal status of persons on board a United Kingdom ship came under close scrutiny; in particular the distinction between "persons engaged on the business of the ship" and "passengers". As a result of the judgement made in this case it has been decided to give the following guidance regarding the status of persons when carried on board United Kingdom ships.

2.   The current legal definition of a passenger is given in Section 26 of the Merchant Shipping Act 1949 which states:

(1) In Part II of the principal Act (ie. the Merchant Shipping Act 1894), in the Merchant Shipping (Safety and Load Lines Conventions) Act, 1932, and in this Act, the expression 'passenger' means any person carried in a ship, except –

(a) a person employed or engaged in any capacity on board the ship on the business of the ship;

(b) a person on board the ship either in pursuance of the obligation laid upon the master to carry shipwrecked, distressed or other persons, or by reason of any circumstance that neither the master nor the owner nor the charterer (if any) could have prevented or forestalled; and

(c) a child under one year of age.

(2) In the Merchant Shipping (Safety and Load Lines Convention), Act 1932, and in this Act, the expression 'passenger steamer' means a steamer carrying more than

---

** The appeal case referred to in this Notice was Secretary of State for Trade v Charles Hector Booth (master of the yawl "Biche") [1984] I All E R [1984] L.I.L Rep p.26.

twelve passengers. (This definition of a passenger steamer was subsequently amended by Section 17(2) of the Merchant Shipping Act 1964).

3.   After carefully studying the Court's judgement of the case it is the Department's view that the only persons who can be considered as being lawfully 'employed or engaged on the business of the ship' are those over the minimum school leaving age (about 16 years) who:

(i) have a contractually binding agreement to serve on the ship in some defined capacity and which could include carrying out such duties under training, or are

(ii) duly signed on members of the crew.

4.   In addition to noting the foregoing, it is recommended that whenever the carriage of passengers is contemplated on any ship the contents of Merchant Shipping Notice No. 913 should be carefully studied.

Department of Transport
Marine Directorate
London WC1V 6LP

October 1985

ANNEX 6

INTERPRETATION OF THE TERM 'PLEASURE YACHT' USED BY THE DEPARTMENT

Legal opinion obtained by the Department as to what type of vessel may be classed as a "pleasure yacht" is that it is "a vessel which is used exclusively for sport and pleasure and which is NOT used for reward, engaged in trade or mercantile activity" (noting that it is the use to which the OWNER or demise charterer puts the vessel which governs its classification).

In considering the interpretation given above, the terms "used for reward" and "engaged in trade or mercantile activity" should be interpreted broadly. Obvious examples would be the carriage of passengers, cargo, stores, equipment etc., and the conducting of survey or photographic exercises for monetary payment. On this basis it follows that the majority of vessels engaged in sea angling, bird watching, scuba diving and sail training should NOT be classified as pleasure yachts.

It should be noted that persons carried on board ship are deemed to be passengers, even if they have paid no fare, unless they are employed or engaged in any capacity on board the ship on the business of the ship. See Merchant Shipping Notice M. 1194, at Annex 5.

It is, of course, appreciated that doubt about the classification of a particular vessel may still exist and if clarification is needed it will be necessary for the owner to submit full details of the vessel and operational intentions. This is, the area of operation, number of persons to be carried, the duties to be undertaken, full details of any fees charged or payments to be made such as crew wages, voyage costs, etc. Such information will then be sent to the Department's solicitors for consideration.

Unless a vessel is classified as a ship of war, a ship solely engaged in fishing or a pleasure yacht it is subject to the requirements of the Merchant Shipping (Load Line) Rules 1968 and must be surveyed and certified accordingly unless it is exempted by virtue of the Merchant Shipping (Load Line)

(Exemption) Order 1968 (SI 1968/1116) as amended by the Merchant Shipping (Load Line) (Exemption) (Amendment) Order 1990 (SI 1990/365).

It should be noted that the expression "solely engaged in fishing" means that the vessel is used for fishing at sea for profit and is entered on the register established under Part II of the Merchant Shipping Act 1988.

The vessel may also be subject to legislation concerning Life Saving Appliances, Fire Extinguishing Appliances, Stability Information, Manning, Radio, Collision Regulations, Crew Accommodation, Machinery Installations, etc.

If a vessel carries more than 12 passengers it also becomes subject to passenger ship regulations and certification.

ANNEX 7

THE MANNING OF SAIL TRAINING SHIPS

This Annex gives information relating to the manning and operation of sail training ships as follows:

Section 1 –   Areas of Application
Section 2 –   Minimum Qualifications of the Master and the additional person to be carried
Section 3 –   Responsibility of Owner for Safe Manning of Vessel
Section 4 –   Keeping a Safe Navigational Watch
Section 5 –   Application of Other Restrictions.

General

Ships of less than 80 GRT or under 24 metres in length carrying less than 24 persons which comply with the requirements of this Code will be exempt from the need to comply fully with the Merchant Shipping (Certification of Deck Officers) Regulations 1985 provided the manning of the ship, when operating in areas described in Section 1 below, is in accordance with the standards given in Section 2.

1. AREAS OF APPLICATION

Sail training ships operating within the following areas should carry at least the qualified personnel shown in paragraph 2 below:–

(a) Unlimited Area.

(b) The Extended European Trade Area.

(c) (i) The Limited European Trading Area;

    (ii) The Mediterranean and Black Seas.

(d) Coastal Waters, being not more than 15 miles from the coast of the country of operation.

(e) Inshore Waters, being not more than 3 miles from the coast and not more than 15 miles, exclusive of any smooth waters, as defined in the Merchant Shipping (Smooth and Partially Smooth Waters) Regulations 1987 from the point of departure.

The areas in (b) and (c)(i) are defined in Appendix A to this Annex and all areas are illustrated in Appendix B.

2. MINIMUM QUALIFICATION OF THE MASTER AND THE ADDITIONAL PERSON TO BE CARRIED.

(a) *Voyages in Unlimited Areas*

The master must hold a RYA/DTp Yachtmaster Ocean Certificate or a DTp Yachtmaster Ocean Certificate.

There should also be on board another person holding a RYA/DTp Yachtmaster Ocean Certificate or a DTp Yachtmaster Ocean Certificate.

(b) *Voyages within the Extended European Trading Area.*

The master must hold a RYA/DTp Yachtmaster Ocean Certificate or a DTp Yachtmaster Ocean Certificate.

There should also be on board a person holding a RYA/DTp Coastal Skipper Certificate.

(c) *Voyages within the Limited European Trading Area and voyages within the Mediterranean and Black Seas.*

The master must hold a RYA/DTp Yachtmaster Offshore Certificate or a DTp Yachtmaster Coastal Certificate.

For ships carrying between 15 and 24 person there should also be on board a person holding a RYA/DTp Coastal Skipper Certificate.

For ships carrying fewer than 15 persons there should also be on board a second person deemed by the master to be experienced.

(d) *Voyages within Coastal Waters*

For ships carrying between 15 and 24 persons the master must hold a RYA/DTp Yachtmaster Offshore Certificate or a DTp Yachtmaster Coastal Certificate.

For ships carrying fewer than 15 persons the master must hold a RYA/DTp Coastal Skipper Certificate.

(e) *Inshore Waters*

For the independent operation of a single dinghy or dayboat the person in charge must hold a RYA Dinghy Instructor Certificate, with Tidal Endorsement.

Dinghies or dayboats operating as a group within safety
boat cover need not carry a qualified person in each boat
but the person in charge of the group must hold a RYA
Dinghy Senior Instructor Certificate, with Tidal
Endorsement.

3. RESPONSIBILITY OF OWNER FOR SAFE MANNING OF VESSEL

It is the responsibility of the owner to ensure that the Master
and where necessary the second-in-command of a ship have,
in addition to any qualifications required in section 2 above,
recent and relevant experience of the type and size of ship
and of the type of operation in which she is engaged. The
possession of a certificate of competence should not, on its
own, be regarded as evidence of ability to command a
specific ship. The owner must also ensure that there are at all
times sufficient experienced crew on board to work the ship,
having regard to the weight of the gear to be handled and the
probable duration of the voyage.

4. KEEPING A SAFE NAVIGATIONAL WATCH

It is the responsibility of the Master to ensure that there is, at
all times, a person with adequate qualifications and
experience in charge of the navigational watch. In taking this
decision the Master should take into account all the factors
affecting the safety of the ship, including:–

(i) the present and forecast state of the weather, visibility
and sea;
(ii) the proximity of navigational hazards;
(iii) the density of traffic in the area.

5. APPLICATION OF OTHER RESTRICTIONS

In addition to the various conditions set out in this Annex,
the owner, operator and master of a sail training ship must
make themselves aware of, and comply with, any other
conditions or restrictions imposed by the Sail Training Ship
Certificate.

APPENDIX A

DEFINITIONS OF "LIMITED EUROPEAN TRADING AREA" AND "EXTENDED EUROPEAN TRADING AREA"

"Limited European Trading Area": an area bounded by a line from a point on the Norwegian coast in latitude 62° North to a point 62° North 02° West: thence to a point 58° North 10° West; thence to a point 54° North 14° West; thence to a point 51° North 14° North West; thence to a point 38° 40' North 10° West; thence to Cape St. Vincent; but excluding all waters which lie to the northward and eastward of a line between Kalmar on the East coast of Sweden and a point on the West coast of Oland in latitude 56° 40' North and from the southern tip of Oland to Gdansk, except between the dates of 1st May and 30th November when the remaining waters of the Baltic Sea are included.

"Extended European Trading Area" an area bounded by a line from Mys Kanin Nos lighthouse on the eastern shore of the White Sea to a Point 72° North 28° 14' East; thence to a point 72° North 24° East; thence to a point 70° 10' North 14° 30' East; thence to a point 62° North 02° West; thence to a point 58° North 10° West; thence to a point 54° North 14° West; thence to a point 33° North 18° 30' West; thence to a point 28° North 19° 15' West; thence to a point 15° North 18° 30' West; thence to Dakar; including the Limited European Trading Area and the Baltic, Mediterranean and Black Seas.

APPENDIX B

FIGURE 7

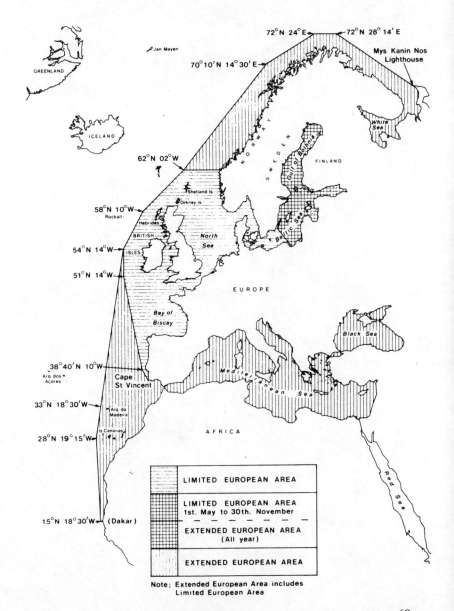

72°N 24'E → 72°N 28°14'E

Mys Kanin Nos Lighthouse

70°10'N 14°30'E →

62°N 02°W

58°N 10°W
Rockall

54°N 14°W

51°N 14°W

38°40'N 10°W
Arq dos Açores

33°N 18°30'W
Arq da Madeira

28°N 19°15'W
Is Canarias

15°N 18°30'W → (Dakar)

Cape St Vincent

GREENLAND

Jan Mayen

ICELAND

Shetland Is

Orkney Is

Hebrides

BRITISH ISLES

North Sea

NORWAY

SWEDEN

Gulf of Bothnia

FINLAND

White Sea

Baltic Sea

Bay of Biscay

EUROPE

Mediterranean Sea

Black Sea

AFRICA

Red Sea

	LIMITED EUROPEAN AREA
	LIMITED EUROPEAN AREA 1st. May to 30th. November
	EXTENDED EUROPEAN AREA (All year)
	EXTENDED EUROPEAN AREA

Note; Extended European Area includes Limited European Area

69

ANNEX 8

DECLARATION OF SURVEY OF A SAIL TRAINING SHIP

Name of Ship ....   Name & Address ....
                            of Owner ....

Official No ....

Port of Registry ....

Gross Tonnage ....

Maximum No. of Persons to   Overall Length ....
be carried ....

Date of Build ....   Hull Identification No. ....

I hereby declare that the above named ship has been surveyed and found to be in accordance with the requirements of the Code of Practice for the Construction, Machinery, Equipment, Stability and Survey of Sail Training Ships between 7 metres and 24 metres in length, published by the Marine Directorate of the Department of Transport, subject to the following conditions:

....

....

....

....

....

....

....

....

Issued at .... on .... 19.....

Name of Surveyor ....

Signature ....

For and on behalf of ....

....

Date ....

71

ANNEX 9

(Seal/Crest and Name of Issuing Authority)

SAIL TRAINING SHIP CERTIFICATE

Name of Ship ....   Name & Address ....
                         of Owner ....

....

Official No ....

Port of Registry ....

Gross Tonnage ....

Maximum No. of Persons to   Overall Length ....
   be carried ....

Date of Build ....   Hull Identification No. ....

This is to certify that the above named ship was surveyed by ....

.... of ....

.... at .... on........................

and found to be in accordance with the requirements of the
Code of Practice for the Construction, Machinery,
Equipment, Stability and Survey of Sail Training Ships
between 7 metres and 24 metres in length, published by the
Marine Directorate of the Department of Transport.

This certificate will remain valid until .... subject
to the ship, its machinery and equipment being efficiently
maintained and inspected annually, and to the following
conditions*:-

....

....

....

....

....

....

....

....
....

Issued at .... on .... 19 .....
For and behalf of ....
Name .... Signature ....
      Date ....
(Note: details of Annual Inspections to be given
overleaf.)
*The permitted area of operation must also be
shown here.

Record of Annual Inspections made to establish the condition
of the ship and its equipment

First Inspection;
Conducted at ....date made ....
Inspected by ....of ....
Signature ....date ....

Second Inspection
Conducted at ....date made ....
Inspected by ....of ....
Signature ....date ....

Third Inspection;
Conducted at ....date made ....
Inspected by ....of ....
Signature ....date ....

Fourth Inspection;
Conducted at ....date made ....
Inspected by ....of ....
Signature ....date ....

Fifth Inspection;
Conducted at ....date made ....
Inspected by ....of ....
Signature ....date ....

Sixth Inspection:
Conducted at ....date made ....
Inspected by ....of.....................
Signature ....date ....

Seventh Inspection;
Conducted at ....date made ....
Inspected by ....of.....................
Signature ....date ....

Eighth Inspection;
Conducted at ....date made ....
Inspected by ....of.....................
Signature ....date ....

Ninth Inspection;
Conducted at ....date made ....
Inspected by ....of.....................
Signature ....date ....

ANNEX 10

SAIL TRAINING SHIP

INSPECTION QUESTIONNAIRE

(for ships less than 15 metres in length and carrying fewer than 15 persons)

This Questionnaire is to be completed by the owner or his managing agent following an annual inspection of a sail training ship – with reference to section 27.4 of the 'Code of Practice for the Construction, Machinery, Equipment, Stability and Survey of Sail Training Ships between 7 metres and 24 metres in length', issued by the Department of Transport.

Name of Ship ....

Official Number ....

Port of Registry ....

Length ....

Owner ....

Address ....

....

....

Managing Agent ....

Address ....

....

....

Sail Training Ship Certificate issued by ....

Date of issue .... Valid until ....

Maximum number of persons permitted to be carried ....

Permitted area of operation ....

Other conditions on certificate ....

1. HULL STRUCTURE AND RIG (Section 4)

The hull structure and rig have been inspected whilst the ship was out of the water and found to be in seaworthy condition.

YES   NO

Have any repairs/alterations been made since last inspection?

YES   NO

If yes, give details:

....

....

....

1.1 Hull Fittings (Sections 5, 6 and 9)

The items listed below have been inspected and are in substantially the same condition as when the ship was last certified. During this inspection all locking devices were checked, all hatchways and closing appliances were hose tested for weather-tightness and all working parts were tested and shown to be in effective condition:

	yes	no	not applicable
(a) Hatchways, Companion hatchways, Cockpit Lockers, Skylights, Cockpit drainage arrangements			....
(b) Portlights, Windows			....
(c) Ventilators, Air pipes			....
(d) All skin fittings			....
(e) Bulwarks, guard rails, freeing ports and guards			....
(f) Stern gear and rudder			....

Give brief details of any repairs or modifications which have
been made to any of the above items;

....

....

....

2. MACHINERY EQUIPMENT (Section 7)

The propelling machinery, its means of starting and its
associated auxiliaries have been inspected and tested and all
are in substantially the same condition as when the ship was
last certified.

YES   NO

2.1 Associated Machinery Equipment (Sections 7, 8, 9 and 10)

The items listed below have been inspected and are in
substantially the same condition as when the ship was last
certified. During this inspection all items were checked to
ensure they were in safe condition and in good working order;

yes   no   not applicable

(a) Starting Motors, Batteries ....

(b) Fuel tank, associated
piping, valves and vents ....

(c) Electrical Lighting System,
Emergency Lighting
System, Generators ....

(d) Steering equipment,
Emergency steering
equipment ....

(e) Bilge pumping and
associated piping ....

Give brief details of any repairs or modifications made to any
of the above items,

....

....

....

3. STABILITY (Section 11 and Annex 13)

Is the stability document on board?   YES   NO

Have any changes been made to the ship
which could affect stability, e.g. removal
or addition of ballast, added equipment,
standard changes, etc?   YES   NO

If yes, give details;

....

....

4. LIFE-SAVING APPLIANCES (LSA)
(Section 13 and Annex 1)

Is the full outfit of LSA, including the
training manual which was presented when
the ship was last certified, still on board?   YES   NO

Has the outfit of LSA, including the items
listed below, been inspected and found to
be in satisfactory condition?   YES   NO

4.1 Liferafts (Annex 1)

Do the liferafts appear to be in sound
condition and are they properly stowed?   YES   NO

When were liferafts last serviced at a
recognised service station? ....

Are liferafts stowed in their correct
positions and, if provided, are the
hydrostatic release units (HRUs) properly
attached to the rafts?   YES   NO

When were HRUs last serviced by
service agent, or replaced? ....

4.2 Lifejackets (Annex 1)

Have all lifejackets been inspected and
found to be in sound condition?   YES   NO

If lifejackets are of the gas inflatable
type when were they last serviced? ....

If lifejackets are of the orally inflatable
type when were they last pressure tested? ....

4.3 Lifebuoys and Danbuoys (Annex 1)
Are lifebuoys or danbuoys in sound
condition?   YES   NO

Self-igniting lights, if replaceable, must be
replaced by their expiry date. Give the
expiry date of those currently on board ....

Have batteries been replaced within
previous 12 months?   YES   NO

4.4 Inflatable Tender (Section 24)
Is the tender in sound condition?   YES   NO   N/A

4.5 Pyrotechnics (Annex 1)
Are all pyrotechnics in a dry and sound
condition?   YES   NO

Parachute rockets   dates of expiry........................

....

Red Hand Flares   dates of expiry........................

....

Buoyant Smoke Signals   dates of expiry........................

....

4.6 Radar Transponders (Annex 1)
Have batteries reached their expiry date?   YES   NO

**5. FIRE FIGHTING EQUIPMENT (Section 14 and Annexes
2, 3 and 4)**
Has a general inspection of the ship been
made in order to establish that the
equipment used and arrangements made to
fight and reduce the risk of fire are in
good condition?   YES   NO

5.1 Fire Fighting Pumps and Associated Piping (Annex 2)
Are the pumps, the associated piping and
fire hoses in good condition?   YES   NO

Has the fire pump been tested?   YES   NO

81

5.2 Fire Extinguishers (Annex 2)

Each extinguisher should be checked for condition annually. Charges should be renewed if deterioration is evident. Gas cartridges should be renewed if loss of gas by mass exceeds 10% of original charge as stamped on cartridge.

Each extinguisher should be given a full service by a competent person at intervals not exceeding 4 years.

In each case the date should be recorded on a tag or label on the extinguisher.

5.2.1 Extinguishers in engine space

Type and identification marking	Capacity	Date of last annual check	Date of last full service
....	....	....	....
....	....	....	....

5.2.2 Extinguishers outside engine space

Type and identification marking	Capacity	Date of last annual check	Date of last full service
....	....	....	....
....	....	....	....
....	....	....	....

5.3 Fire Blanket (Annex 2)

Is the fire blanket on board and in apparent good order?   YES   NO   N/A

5.4 LPG Appliances (Annex 4)

Has the LPG system and its associated equipment and piping been inspected and found to be in safe condition and working order?   YES   NO   N/A

Has the gas detector been tested and found to be in good working order?   YES   NO   N/A

Are all enclosed spaces including the bilges checked daily for the presence of LPG using the gas detector?   YES   NO   N/A

6. RADIO EQUIPMENT AND EPIRBs (Section 16)

Is all the radio equipment in working
order?   YES   NO

When was the equipment last examined by
a competent radio engineer? ....

Does the EPIRB appear to be in working
order?   YES   NO

7. NAVIGATION LIGHTS, SHAPES AND SOUND SIGNALS (SECTION 17)

Are all the necessary nagivation lights,
shapes and sound signals on board and in
working order?   YES   NO

8. NAVIGATIONAL EQUIPMENT (SECTION 18)

Are all charts up to date?   YES   NO

Is all the navigational equipment in
working order?   YES   NO

When was this equipment last examined by a
competent person? ....

When were magnetic compass deviations last verified? ....

9. MEASURING AND MISCELLANEOUS EQUIPMENT (Sections 19 and 20)

Are all the items of equipment listed below on board and in
working order?

	YES	NO
Anchors and cables	....	
Barometer and anemometer	....	
Wire cutting equipment	....	
Signalling torch, radar reflector	....	
Safety harnesses, boarding ladders	....	
Storm sails	....	

10. MEDICAL STORES (Section 23 and Annexes 14 and 15)
Are the medical stores complete and in
sound condition?   YES   NO

I certify that I have diligently checked the ship, its machinery
and equipment and, to the best of my knowledge, the
answers and information given to the questions in this
document are correct.

Signed .... Date ....

for and on behalf of ....

ANNEX 11

BOATBUILDER'S DECLARATION FOR A UNITED KINGDOM SAIL TRAINING SHIP

Name of Ship .... Name & Address ....
of Owner ....

Official No ....

Port of Registry ....

Gross Tonnage ....

Maximum No. of Persons to   Overall Length ....
be carried ....

Date of Build .... Hull Identification No. ....

We hereby declare that the above mentioned ship has been
supplied by us in accordance with the following provisions of
the Code of Practice for the Construction, Machinery,
Equipment, Stability and Survey of Sail Training Ships
between 7 metres and 24 metres in length published by the
Department of Transport:

* ALL PROVISIONS *PROVISIONS/CLAUSE NO.	BUILDERS INITIALS/ SIGNATURE
....	....
....	....
....	....
....	....

*Delete as applicable

Signed ....
for and on behalf of ...... (BOATBUILDERS)
....
....
on .... 19 ....

This declaration does not in itself provide full compliance
with the Code, nor do its contents affect the statutory rights
of the customer.

85

ANNEX 12

OWNER'S DECLARATION FOR A UNITED KINGDOM SAIL TRAINING SHIP

Name of vessel ....

Registration

Number ....

Owner/

Managing ....

Agent

Address ....

....

....

DETAILS OF VESSEL

LENGTH ....

MAXIMUM NUMBER OF PERSONS TO BE CARRIED .....

LIMITATION ON OPERATING AREA

LIMITATION IMPOSED BY	LIMITATION ACCEPTED
STABILITY – SECTION 11	....
LIFE-SAVING APPLIANCES – SECTION 13	....
RADIO EQUIPMENT – SECTION 16	....
VENTILATION – SECTION 21.1	....
MANNING – SECTION 26	....

FOR SHIPS OF NEW CONSTRUCTION
A builder's declaration of compliance with sections 4 – 8.1, 8.3 – 11, 14, 15.2, 17 (for lights), 21 – 22.2 and 22.4 – 22.6 is attached.

OWNER'S/MANAGING AGENT'S DECLARATION

I have taken all possible care in answering the questions in this document and to the best of my knowledge the answers are correct. I believe that the vessel complies with the Code of Practice as set out in this document and apply for exemption from the Merchant Shipping rules and regulations for a vessel of Class XI for the year 19 ....

I undertake to maintain the vessel in sound and seaworthy condition and to inform the Sail Training Ship Certifying Authority of any changes to the structure or equipment of the vessel and of any collision, grounding or damage encountered by the vessel.

Signed .... Date ....

Section

8. *Electrical arrangements*

8.2 Describe system of emergency lighting:

....

....

....

16. *Radio Equipment*

16.1 *Radio Installation*

List the VHF transmitting and receiving equipment fitted.

....

....

16.2 *EPIRBS*

What is the make, model and serial number of the EPIRB? ....

....

88

17. *Shapes*

List the shapes carried on board:

Shape	*Size*
1. Anchor ball	Diameter ....
2. Motor sailing cone	Diameter of base ....
	Height ....

18. *Navigational Equipment*

18.1 *Compass*

List the steering and hand bearing compasses carried:

....

....

....

Date when magnetic compass deviations were last verified

....

Please attach copy of latest deviation card.

Steel Ships

State the size and position of soft iron correctors:

Corrector	*Size and Distance from Centre*
1. Kelvin spheres	....
2. Flinders Bar	....

Means of taking bearings

Describe the compass used for taking bearings.

....

....

18.2 *Navigational Equipment*

State navigational equipment carried.

Equipment	Make and Model
1. Radio Direction Finder	....
2. Decca	....
3. Loran	....
4. Satnav	....
5. Echo Sounder	....
6. Log	....

19.1 *Nautical Publications*

Ships of 12 metres or more in length

List the edition of each of the following publications carried:

Publication	Edition/Supplement Date
1. Sailing Directions	....
	....
	....
2. Admiralty Tide Tables	....
3. Admiralty Lists of Radio Signals	Vol ....
	....
4. Area of Chart Coverage	....
	....
	....
5. Charts corrected to weekly edition of notices to mariners	No .... Of ....

19.2 *Signalling Lamp*

Make and model:

....

19.3 *Radar Reflector*

Make and model of radar reflector carried:

....

....

19.4 *Measuring Instruments*

Instrument	*Make and Model*
1. Barometer	....
2. Anemometer	....

19.5 *Wire Cutting Equipment*

Describe the wire cutting equipment carried:

....

....

20. *Anchors and Cables*

Overall length of vessel: ....

	Type	*Weight*	*Cable*			
			Chain		*Warp*	
			Length	*Dia.*	*Length*	*Dia.*
Bower	....	....	....	....	....	....
Kedge	....	....	....	....	....	....

If anchor weighs more than 30 kg, what type of windlass is provided?

....

....

22.3 *Safety Harnesses*

Manufacturer	*Type*	*Number*
....	....	....
....	....	....
....	....	....

22.7 *Boarding Ladder or Scrambling Net*

What is the depth below the operational waterline of the lowest rung of the boarding ladder or lowest part of the scrambling net?

....

25. *Storm Sails*

For Bermudan rigged vessels:

Tri-sail or deep-reefing mainsail.

<table>
<tr><td></td><td>Full hoist luff-length of mainsail (P)</td><td>..........</td></tr>
<tr><td></td><td>Length of foot of mainsail (E)</td><td>..........</td></tr>
<tr><td></td><td>Trisail Permitted max area ($0.175 \times P \times E$)</td><td>..........</td></tr>
<tr><td>EITHER</td><td>Measured Tri-sail area</td><td>..........</td></tr>
<tr><td>OR</td><td>Deep reef in mainsail reducing luff length to no more than 60% of full hoist.</td><td></td></tr>
<tr><td>OR</td><td>Actual luff-length with deep reef</td><td>..........</td></tr>
</table>

Heavy weather jib and storm jib

<table>
<tr><td>Height of fore triangle (IG)</td><td>..........</td></tr>
<tr><td>Max permitted area of heavy weather jib $0.135 \times IG^2$</td><td>..........</td></tr>
<tr><td>Measured area of heavy weather jib</td><td>..........</td></tr>
<tr><td>Max permitted area of storm jib $0.05 \times IG^2$, max permitted luff length $0.65 \times IG$.</td><td>..........</td></tr>
<tr><td>Measured area of storm jib</td><td>..........</td></tr>
<tr><td>Measured luff length of storm jib</td><td>..........</td></tr>
</table>

ANNEX 1: Life Saving Appliances

Liferaft(s)

Manufacturer	Type	Capacity	Last serviced
....	....	....	....
....	....	....	....
....	....	....	....

HRUs

Manufacturer	Type	Last Serviced*	Expiry Date*
....	....	....	....
....	....	....	....

(* As appropriate)

Lifebuoys

Manufacturer	Type
....	....
....	....

Danbuoy

Height of flag above waterline ....
Self igniting lights:

Manufacturer	Type
....	....

Buoyant Lifeline

Length ....

Lifejackets

Manufacturer	Type	Number	Last Serviced/ Pressure Tested
....	....	....	....
....	....	....	....
....	....	....	....

Pyrotechnics

Type	Number	Manufacturer	Expiry Date
1. Rocket Parachute Flares	....	....	....
2. Red Hand Flares	....	....	....
3. Buoyant smoke	....	....	....

Training Manuals
Number:

Instruction for on-board maintenance   YES/NO
(where retained on board)

Portable two-way radio-telephone set

Manufacturer	Type	Serial No.
....	....	....

Radar transponder

Manufacturer	Type	Serial No.
....	....	....

ANNEX 2: Fire Fighting Appliances

Fire Pumps

Type and Capacity:

....

....

Engine Space Fire Extinguisher

Extinguishing agent and fire rating ....

....

Date of last annual check ....

Date of last full service ....

Multi-purpose Fire Extinguishers

Manu-facturer	Fire Rating	Stowage	Date of	
			Last Annual Check	Last Full Service
....	....	....	....	....
....	....	....	....	....
....	....	....	....	....
....	....	....	....	....

Fire Buckets

Capacity	Stowage
....	....
....	....
....	....

Fire Blanket

Manufacturer	Model
....	....

ANNEX 13

RYA SAIL TRAINING OPERATIONAL SCHEME (STOPS)

STOPS NUMERAL = FBS* FDL* FBD* FSDBL* FR* FK* FEP* FDAY* FVA

Where:

FBS (Factor, Base Size). Basic seaworthiness may be considered to be directly related to size, since the relative scale of wind forces and wave action diminishes with increasing ship size. FBS is modified by the application of the following safety related factors to take account of variation from the norm.

FDL (Factor, Displacement Length). Within limits, heavy displacement for length may be considered desirable for seaworthiness because light displacement for length can initiate control and stability problems in heavy conditions.

FBD (Factor, Beam Displacement). Large beam, particularly related to low displacement and topside flare, has been shown to accentuate the risk both of wave induced capsize and inverted stability. High Beam/Displacement ratios are therefore considered less seaworthy whilst a very low ratio implies a lack of form stability.

FSDBL (Factor, Sail Area, Displacement, Beam, Length). Power to carry sail is related to displacement but, due to physical scaling laws, the value must also be linked to size.

FR (Factor, Rig). Ease of handling and of shortening sail and the greater structural integrity of sturdy rigs not requiring skilled control are recognised as features of seaworthiness.

FK (Factor, Keel). Normal ballast stability may be reduced by the use of centreboards and drop keels.

FEP (Factor, Engine and Propeller). The availability of an efficient engine installation in times of emergency is regarded as an item enhancing seaworthiness and safety.

FDAY (Factor, Dayboat). This applies to dayboats (boats without guardrails or self-draining cockpits). It cannot be used in sail training ships.

FVA (Factor, Vanishing Angle). Derived from the Screen in section 11.1.2.4 which estimates the angle of vanishing stability from the parameters displaced volume, beam, ballast ratio and canoe body depth. The estimate is compared with the required range for the proposed area of operation, set out in the table in section 11.1.2.6. The RORC SSS Numeral replaces this with a factor based on the righting lever at 90°, derived from a practical inclining test.

The modifying factors are, where necessary, limited to maximum and minimum values so that a single favourable factor is prevented from exerting undue influence.

The precise derivation of the respective factors and the resulting STOPS numeral is shown in the following simple BASIC computer programme:

BASIC PROGRAM LISTING

1000 STOPS.BAS version 1,2 23 Sept 89 COPYRIGHT RYA/RORC
1010 IF E>P/3 THEN MAINSAIL=(P*P/3*.6)+(P*(E-P/3)*.4) ELSE
MAINSAIL=(P*P/3*.6)-(P*(P/3-E)*.2)   : mainsail area
1020 IF LP>J THEN JIB=(FL*J*.55)+(FL*(LP-J)*.3)
  ELSE JIB=FL*J*.55   : headsail area
1030 MIZZEN=PY*EY*.55   : mizzen main area
1040 JIBY=FLY*LY*.55   : mizzen head area
1050 SA=(MAINSAIL+JIB)   : normal sloop area
1060 IF RT=2 THEN SA=
((MAINSAIL+JIB)+.6*(MIZZEN+JIBY))   : ketch or yawl area
1070 IF RT=3 THEN SA=
((MAINSAIL+JIB)+.8*(MIZZEN+JIBY))   : schooner area
1080 IF RT=4 THEN SA=(MAINSAIL+MIZZEN):   cat area
1090 IF ST=2 THEN SA=SA*.8   : gaff area correction
1100 V=DISP/1025   : volume of displacement
1110 W=DISP-(62*LA)   : boat weight empty
1120 L=(LA+LW)/2   : corrected length
1130 FBS=(3*L)+.25   : base size factor
1140 S1=2830*L/W   : length/disp screen
                                             (from AYF)
1150 S2=(670*LA-4670)/W   : length/disp screen for
                                             ULDBs
1160 IF S1>6 THEN DL1=2.465/(SI^.5)   : lighter than normal
1170 IF S1<=6 THEN DL1=6/S1   : heavier than normal
1180 IF S2>1 THEN DL2=1/(1.5*S2)   : mainly for long boats
1190 IF S2>1 AND DL2<DL1 THEN DL1=DL2   : lower value applied
1200 IF DL1<.6 THEN DL1=.6   : lower limit
1210 IF DL1>1.2 THEN DL1=1.2   : upper limit
1220 S3=(40*W/L^3)+6*L   : relative DLR scaled for size
1230 DL3=1-(105/S3-.35)   :
1240 IF DL3<.75 THEN DL3=.75   : lower limit
1250 IF DL3>.1.2 THEN DL3=1.2   : upper limit
1260 FDL=(DL1+DL3)/2   : mean disp/length value used
1270 S4=3.28*BM/((W*2.21/64)^(1/3))   : beam/disp (USYRU Screen)
1280 IF S4>2.43 THEN FBD=14.3489/S4^3
ELSE FBD=1   : inverted stability
1290 IF S4<1.45 THEN FBD=S4^2/2.1025   : narrow beam
1300 IF FBD<.75 THEN FBD=.75   : lower limit
1310 S5=(W*BM)/(LW*SA^1.5)   : sa, disp, b, lwl factor
1320 IF S5>=4 THEN FSDBL=.8+(.05*S5)   : low area rigs
1330 IF S5<4 THEN FSDBL=1.5-(2/S5)   : high area rigs
1340 IF FSDBL<.8 THEN FSDBL=.8   : lower limit
1350 IF FSDBL>1.05 THEN FSDBL=1.05   : upper limit
1360 FR=1:FK=1:FEP=.92:FDAY=1   : default values
1370 IF PY>0 and EY>0 THEN FR=1.05   : for twin masted rigs
1380 IF RT=4 THEN FR=1.02*FR   : for cutter rig
1390 IF NR+HY=0 THEN FR=FR+.015   : for simple rig
1400 IF DS=0 THEN FR=FR+.07   : no downwind sails
1410 IF DS=2 THEN FR=FR+.03   : cruising chute only

99

```
1420 IF GR=0 THEN FR=FR-.02          : no guardrails
1430 IF KT>3 THEN FK=.85             : for drop keel or c/b
1440 IF KT>1 THEN BAL=BAL*.8         : bilge keel ballast adjustment
1450 IF ET=0 THEN FEP=.92:GOTO 1490  : no engine
1460 IF ET=1 THEN FEP=1:GOTO 1490    : outboard motor
1470 IF ET+PF=3 THEN FEP=1.05        : outboard motor
1480 IF ET+PF=4 THEN FEP=1.08        : no engine
1490 IF DB=1 THEN FDAY=.8            : dayboat factor
1500 R=BAL/DISP                      : ballast ratio
1510 SV=BM^2/(R*T*V^(1/3))           : estimated range screen
                                       value
1520 EST=110+400/(SV-10)             : estimated range
1530 IF EST<0 OR EST>180 THEN EST=180 : limits of estimated range
1540 REQ1=90+60*(24-LA)/17           : required range for cats 1&0
1550 REQ2=90+60*(24-LA)/20           : required range for
                                       category 2
1560 REQ3=90+60*(24-LA)/25           : required range for
                                       category 3
1570 FVA1=(EST/REQ1)^3               : vanishing angle factor 1&0
1580 FVA2=(EST/REQ2)^3               : vanishing angle factor 2
1590 FVA3=(EST/REQ3)^3               : vanishing angle factor 3
1600 IF FVA1>1.25 THEN FVA1=1.25     : upper limit
1610 IF FVA2>1.25 THEN FVA2=1.25     : upper limit
1620 IF FVA3>1.25 THEN FVA3=1.25     : upper limit
1630 SSS=FBS*FDL*FBD*FSDBL*FR*FK*FEP
*FDAY                                : SSS with no stability factor
1640 STOPS1=INT(SSS*FVA1)+5          : level 1&0 STOPS numeral
1650 STOPS2=INT(SSS*FVA2)+5          : level 2 STOPS numeral
1660 STOPS3=INT(SSS*FVA3)+5          : level 3 STOPS numeral
1670 CAT$="0"                        : category 0
1680 IF STOPS1<50 THEN CAT$="1"      : category 1
1690 IF STOPS1<40 THEN CAT$="2"      : category 2
1700 IF STOPS2<30 THEN CAT$="3"      : category 3
1710 IF STOPS3<20 THEN CAT$="NIL"    : not suitable
1720 PRINT CAT$:END
```

Where:–

E	=	mainsail foot length
P	=	mainsail luff length
LP	=	headsail diagonal luff to clew
J	=	distance between headsail tack and mast
FL	=	forestay length
EY	=	mizzen main foot length
PY	=	mizzen main luff length
FLY	=	mizzen forestay length
LY	=	mizzen head diagonal luff to clew
RT	=	rig type: 1 = sloop
		2 = yawl or ketch
		3 = schooner
		4 = cat

100

ST   = sail type: 1 = bermudan
                      2 = gaff
                      3 = wishbone
DISP = displacement fully rigged and equipped
LA   = length overall
LW   = length waterline
BM   = maximum beam
NR   = number of runners
HY   = number of hydraulics
GR   = guard rails: 0 = not fitted
                       1 = fitted
KT   = keel type: 1 = single
                      2 = twin
                      3 = triple
                      4 = lifting
DB   = dayboat: 0 = not a dayboat
                      1 = is a dayboat
BAL   = ballast
ET   = engine type: 0 = no engine
                      1 = outboard
                      2 = inboard
PF   = propeller type:1 = folding/feathering
                      2 = fixed bladed
T   = 1/8 buttock depth
CAT$ = category of operation

ANNEX 14

Revised Scale II for sail training ships between 7 and 24 metres in length carrying more than 8 persons within the Limited Trading Area and elsewhere on a voyage not exceeding 100 miles

NAME OF MEDICINE (ordering name in small letters)	ORDERING SIZE	QUANTITY REQUIRED
ACTIVATED CHARCOAL – Activated charcoal effervescent granules	5 gm sachet	10
ADRENALINE – Adrenaline acid tartrate injection 1.8 mg in 1 ml [1 in 1000]	0.5 ml ampoule	5
ALUMINIUM ACETATE – Aluminium acetate ear drops 13%	10 ml bottle with dropper	1
ANAESTHETIC EYE DROPS – Amethocaine 0.5%	In a single dose applicator	20
ANTIBIOTIC EAR DROPS[a] – Ear drops containing in each ml neomycin 3 400 units, polymixin B sulphate 10 00 units, hydro-cortisone 10 mg	5 ml dropper bottle	1
ASPIRIN – Dispersible aspirin	300 mg dispsersible tablet	100
ATROPINE – Atropine sulphate injections 1 mg in 1 ml	1 ml ampoule	5
BENZOIC ACID – Benzoic acid compound ointment (benzoic acid 6%; salicylic acid 3%, in emulsifying ointment). Often called Whitfield's ointment.	50 mg	5
BURN CREAM – Silver sulphadiazine cream 1% w/w	50 ml tube	4
CALAMINE LOTION – Calamine 15% lotion	100 ml bottle	1

NAME OF MEDICINE (ordering name in small letters)	ORDERING SIZE	QUANTITY REQUIRED
CETRIMIDE CONCENTRATE – Centrimide Concentrate 40%	100 ml bottle	2
CHLORAMPHENICOL – Chloramphenicol eye ointment 1%	4 gm dispenser	5
CHLOROQUINE – either chloroquine sulphate 200 mg tablet (150 mg of chloroquine); or chloroquine phosphate 250 mg tablet (155 mg of chloroquine base)	200/250 mg tablets	500[b]
CHLORPHENIRAMINE – (1) Chlorpheniramine maleate – (2) Chlorpheniramine maleate injection 10 mg in 1 ml	4 mg tablet 1 ml ampoule	30 5
CHLORPROMAZINE – (1) Chlorpromazine hydrochoride – (2) Chlorpromzaine hydrochoride injection 25 mg in 1 ml	25 mg tablet 1 ml apoule	100 2
CODEINE LINCTUS – Codeine phosphate 15 mg in 5 ml linctus	200 ml bottle	2
CO-TRIMOXAZOLE – Co-trimoxazole (sulphamethoxazole 400 mg trimethoprim 80 mg)	480 mg tablet	50
CYCLIZINE – Cyclizine lactate 50 mg in 1 ml	1 ml ampoule	5
DIAZEPAM – (1) Diazepam – (2) Diazepam injection 5 mg in 1 ml	5 mg tablet 10 ml ampoule	5 2
DIHYDROCODEINE – Dihydrocodeine tartrate	30 mg tablet	100
FRUSEMIDE – (1) Frusemide – (2) Frusemide injection, 10 mg in 1 ml	40 mg tablet 2 ml ampoule	20 5
GLYCERYL TRINITRATE – Glyceryl trinitrate	0.5 mg tablet	100
HYDROCORTISONE OINTMENT – Hydrocortisone 1% ointment	15 mg container	5

NAME OF MEDICINE (ordering name in small letters)	ORDERING SIZE	QUANTITY REQUIRED
HYOSCINE HYDROBROMIDE – Hyoscine hydrobromide	0.3 mg tablet	100
LIGNOCAINE – Lignocaine hydrochloride 1% (plain) 20 mg in 2 ml	2 ml ampoule	5
MAGNESIUM TRISILICATE – Magnesium trisilicate (magnesium trisilicate 250 mg, dried aluminium hydroxide gel 120 mg)	370 gm compound tablet	100
MALOPRIM – Maloprim (pyrimethamine 12.5 mg and dapsone 100 mg)	112.5 mg tablet	360[b]
METRONIDAZOLE – Metronidazole	200 mg tablet	60
MORPHINE – Morphone sulphate injection 15 mg in 1 ml	1 ml ampoule	5
NITRAZEPAM – Nitrazepam	5 mg tablet	10
OIL OF CLOVES – Clove oil	10 ml bottle	1
PARACETAMOL – Paracetamol	500 mg tablet	250
PENCILLIN V – Phenoxymethyl penicillin	250 mg tablet	60
PETROLEUM JELLY – Soft paraffin	50 gm container	2
POTASSIUM PERMANGANATE – Potassium permanganate crystals	10 gm container	1
PREDNISOLONE [a] – (1) Prednisolone – (2) Prednisolone injection 25 mg in 1 ml	5 mg tablets 5 ml vial	60 1
PROGUANIL – Proguanil hydrochloride	100 mg tablet	1000[b]

NAME OF MEDICINE (ordering name in small letters)	ORDERING SIZE	QUANTITY REQUIRED
SALBUTAMOL – Salbutamol aerosol inhaler unit, giving 100 micrograms per metered inhalation	200 dose container	1
SALT TABLETS – Sodium choride and glucose enteric coated	650 mg tablet	500[c]
SODIUM BICARBONATE – Sodium bicarbonate	100 gm	1
SURGICAL SPIRIT – Surgical spirit	250 ml	1
TETRACYCLINE – Tetracycline hydrochloride	250 mg tablet	100
WATER FOR INJECTION – Water for injection	2 ml ampoule	10
ZINC OINTMENT – Zinc oxide 15% in a simple ointment	25 gm container	1

PART 2 – INSTRUMENTS APPLIANCES AND MEASURING EQUIPMENT

Name of item and Ordering Description	QUANTITY REQUIRED
CANVAS ROLL FOR INSTRUMENTS to contain the surgical instruments	1
EYE LOOP Disposable, of nylon with wooden handle	2
FLUORESCEIN STRIPS Fluorescein sodium 1% paper eye test strips	100
FORCEPS of stainless steel throughout (1) Epilation with oblique ends, 12.5 cm (2) Spencer Well's 12.5 cm (3) Tissue forceps, 12.5 cm, 1–2 teeth	1 1 1
GUEDEL AIRWAY Conforming to British Standards Institution BS 2927 published on 29/11/57 (1) Size 4 (2) Size 3 (3) Size 1	1 1 1
KIDNEY DISH Size 250 mm conforming to British Standards Institution BS1823 published on 15/6/73 for stainless steel; or on 28/2/77 for sterilisable plastic	1
LOTION BOWL Size at least 200 mm by 90 mm to BS 1823 for stainless steel, or to BS 5452 for sterilisable plastic, to be lettered "medical" (for BS standards see entry above for kidney dish)	1
MAGNIFYING GLASS 7.5 cm diameter on handle	1
MEASURES Measuring spoon size 5 ml of plastic conforming to British Standards Institution Standard BS 3221/6 1985	50
NECK COLLAR Adjustable fractured (etc) neck – adult size. Set of 3: small, medium and large	1

Name of item and Ordering Description	QUANTITY REQUIRED

RAZOR
Disposable, pack of 5 — 1

RESUSCITATOR, MOUTH TO MOUTH
Short oral airway to non-return valve, of the Brook Airway type — 2

SCALPEL AND BLADE SET
Blades and scalpels size 23, sterile, disposable — 6

SCISSORS
(1) Of stainless steel throughout. Size about 18 cm, one blade sharp-pointed and the other round-ended; conforming to British Standards Institution BS 3646 published on 19/7/63 — 1
(2) Size 12.5 cm both blades sharp-pointed — 1

SPLINTS
(1) Set of common splints — 1
(2) Liston's thigh splint – 140 cm — 1

SUTURE AND NEEDLE – PACK
Sterile, non-absorbable, sutures BP of mono-filament nylon or silk, swaged to a 26 mm, and 40 mm, half circle needle with a cutting edge. Each needle and suture to be in a sealed pack.
(1) 26 mm half circle needle — 1
(2) 40 mm half circle needle — 1
(3) Sterile absorbable sutures BP of catgut swaged to a 40 mm half circle cutting needle — 1

SYRINGE AND NEEDLE, HYPODERMIC – PACK
Sterile disposable, conforming to British Standards Institution Standard BS 5081 published on 30/6/76, each syringe and needle in a sealed pack.
– 2 ml syringe with a 0.8 mm (2 SWG) × 4 cm needle — 10

THERMOMETERS
To give the temperature in degrees C, or degrees C and degrees F. Each thermometer, with instructions as to use, to be in a strong metal or strong plastic case, and to conform to British Standards Institution Standard BS 691 published on 31/12/79
(1) Ordinary range clinical thermometer stubby bulb pattern — 2
(2) Ordinary range rectal thermometer, thermometer and its case clearly marked for rectal use — 1

Name of item and Ordering Description	QUANTITY REQUIRED

TORCH SET
Pencil or other torch suitable for examining eyes, with batteries and one spare bulb, in a suitable box — 1

URINE TESTING EQUIPMENT
(1) Urine test sticks, sugar – in the manufacturer's container with instructions — 50
(2) Urine test sticks – Ketones – in the manufacturer's container with instructions — 50

PART 3 – BANDAGES, COTTON WOOL AND DRESSINGS

Name of item and Ordering Description	QUANTITY REQUIRED

BANDAGES

Each bandage to be individually wrapped

(1) Crepe, BP, 7.5 cm × 4.5 m when stretched 2

(2) Elastic adhesive BP, 7.5 cm × 4 m 1

(3) Triangular of calico, BP, with 2 sides of about 90 cm and a base of about 127 cm 4

(4) Tubular gauze bandage, seamless, of a size suitable for finger dressings, a length of 20 m with applicator 1

(5) Conforming bandage, 5 cm × 3.5 m BP 4

(6) Conforming bandage, 7.5 cm × 3.5 m BP 6

BUTTERFLY CLOSURES

Adhesive skin closures, length approximately 5 cm, individually sealed sterile in a container 20

COTTON WOOL

Absorbent cotton and viscose wadding, BP, in a roll, in a damp proof packaging

(1) Package containing 15 gm, sterile 15

(2) Package containing 100 gm, unsterile 1

DRESSINGS

All dressings are to be individually wrapped and in a strong and suitable container

(1) Sterile paraffin gauze dressing, BP, size 10 cm × 10 cm individually wrapped 20

(2) Standard BPC dressings. The containers for these dressings should each bear a label with instructions covering the following points:

> Open by pulling tabs. Avoid touching wound and do not finger the face of the sterilised pad. Place pad over wound, retain hold of short end of bandage, wind remainder firmly and tie in a knot.

(i) Small plain wound dressing, standard no 13 BPC 5

(ii) Medium plain wound dressing, standard no 14 BPC 5

(iii) Large plain wound dressing, standard no 15 BPC 5

DRESSING STRIP

Elastic adhesive medicated dressing strip BPC, 6 cm × 1 m in a packet 1

Name of item and Ordering Description	QUANTITY REQUIRED
GAUZE Packet containing one piece of sterile absorbent cotton gauze BP, size 30 cm × 90 cm	6
GAUZE, PADS Packet containing 5 sterile gauze pads BP size 7.5 cm × 7.5 cm	10
SUSPENSORY BANDAGE Large size	1
ZINC OXIDE TAPE Zinc oxide	1

PART 4 – SUNDRIES AND PUBLICATIONS

Name of item and Ordering Description	QUANTITY REQUIRED

BAG, BODY
Large size; designed to hold a dead person in a refrigerator up to 14 days or in a cool place for up to 5 days — 1

BUDS
Of viscose or cotton wool, in a container — 100

CHLORINE COMPOUND
In reclosable air-tight containers, sufficient to chlorinate the potable water tanks and associated systems – compounds and quantities to comply with the procedures, etc stated in the latest edition of "The Ship Captain's Medical Guide" or a Merchant Shipping Notice amending those procedures, etc. — YES

CONTAINERS
Airtight, for the dispensing of tablets – 20 tablet size — 10

EYE BATHS — 1

EYE – SHADES
With elastic head band, robust quality throughout — 2

FINGER STALLS
With tapes, of robust material throughout two or more sizes — 2

FIRST AID KIT
The following to be in a damp proof strong canvas bag, satchel, or box, with a strap for carrying: — 1
(1) 4 × triangular bandages, with sides of about 90 cm and a base of about 127 cm
(2) 6 × standard dressings no 8 or 13 BPC
(3) 2 × standard dressings no 9 or 14 BPC
(4) 2 × extra large sterile unmedicated dressings, 28 cm × 17.5 cm
(5) 6 medium size safety pins, rustless
(6) 20 assorted elastic adhesive dressing strips medicated BPC
(7) 2 sterile eye pads with attachment
(8) 2 × packages containing 15 grammes sterile cotton wool
(9) 5 pairs of large, disposable, polythene gloves

GLOVES
Large, of polythene, disposable — 25

Name of item and Ordering Description	QUANTITY REQUIRED
HOT WATER BOTTLE Of rubber, with a fabric cover, size about 20 cm × 30 cm	1
INSECTICIDE In a hand sprayer – spray containers of the standard domestic size[d]	1
LABELS (1) Plain self-adhesive, about 5 cm × 3 cm (2) Tags for patients who have been given morphine	25 5
NAIL BRUSH Of strong sterilisable plastic throughout	1
SPECTACLES – DARK Of robust material throughout	1
SAFETY PINS Rustless, size 5 cm	12
TOWELS Paper, disposable, hand size	100
PUBLICATIONS (a) "The Ship Captain's Medical Guide" – 21st or latest subsequent edition	1
(b) DTp form SCMG/3, visit to doctor form[e]	10
(c) A copy of the Regulations referred to in Merchant Shipping Notice No 1319[e]	1
(d) A copy of Merchant Shipping Notice No M1319 and subsequent admendments	1
(e) Controlled drugs register	1

NOTES

[a] To be used ONLY on medical advice and to be labelled accordingly.

[b] Only required when the vessel is proceeding to or operating in a malarial area as defined in Schedule 3 of M1319.

[c] Only required when the vessel is proceeding to or operating in tropical waters.

[d] A pre-pracked press - button pressure canister may be used in lieu

[e] These forms are available from HMSO bookshops.

ANNEX 15

Scale IV: for ships on voyages not exceeding 72 hours duration plying between ports in the British Isles and for ships carrying not more than eight persons between ports in the British Isles and ports on the Continent of Europe between the River Elbe and Brest

Part 1 – Medicines

NAME OF MEDICINE (Ordering name is in small letters)	ORDERING SIZE	QUANTITIES REQUIRED
ASPIRIN		
– Dispersible aspirin	300mg dispersible tablet	100
CALAMINE LOTION		
– 15% lotion	100ml bottle	1
CETRIMIDE CONCENTRATE		
– Centrimide concentrate 40%	100ml bottle	2
CHLORAMPHENICOL		
– Chloramphenicol eye ointment 1%	4gm dispenser	1
CODEINE LINCTUS		
– Codeine phosphate 15mg in 5 ml linctus	200ml bottle	1
DIAZEPAM		
– (1) Diazepam	5mg tablet	5
DIHYDROCODEINE		
– Dihydrocodeine tartrate	30mg tablet	10
HYOSCINE HYDROBROMIDE		
– Hyoscine hydrobromide	0.3mg tablet	50
MAGNESIUM TRISILICATE		
– Magnesium trisilicate (Magnesium trisilicate, 250mg, dried aluminium hydroxide gel 120mg)	370mg compound tablet	100
OIL OF CLOVES		
– Clove oil	10ml bottle	1
PARACETAMOL		
– Paracetamol	500mg tablet	100

NAME OF MEDICINE (Ordering name is in small letters)	ORDERING SIZE	QUANT-ITIES REQUIRED
PENICILLIN V – Phenoxymethyl penicillin	250mg tablet	60
PETROLEUM JELLY – Soft paraffin	50 gm container	1
POTASSIUM PERMANGANATE – Potassium permanganate crystals	10gm container	1
ZINC OINTMENT – Zinc oxide 15% in a simple ointment	25gm container	1

PART 2 – INSTRUMENTS, APPLIANCES AND MEASURING EQUIPMENT

Note: The packaging for any item on these scales should, where practicable, include the information given in the ordering description below.

Name of Item & Ordering Description	Quantities required
FORCEPS Of stainless steel throughout (1) Epilation with oblique ends, 12.5 cm	1
GUEDEL AIRWAY Conforming to British Standards Institution BS 2927 published on 29.11.57 (1) Size 4	1
SCISSORS (1) Of stainless steel throughout. Size about 18cm, one blade sharp-pointed and the other round-ended; conforming to British Standards Institution Standard BS 3646 published on 19.7.63	1
SPLINTS (1) Set of common splints	1

PART 3 – BANDAGES, COTTON WOOL AND DRESSINGS

Note: The packaging for any item on these scales should, where practicable, include the information given in the ordering description for that item.

Name of Item & Ordering Description	Quantities required
COTTON WOOL Absorbent cotton & viscose wadding, BP, in a roll, in damp proof packaging.	
(1) Package containing 15gm, sterile	10
(2) Packaging containing 100gm, unsterile	1
DRESSINGS All dressings are to be individually wrapped and in a strong and suitable container.	
(1) Sterile paraffin gauze dressing, BP, size 10cm × 10cm individually wrapped	10
(2) Standard BPC dressings. The containers for these dressings should each bear a label with instructions covering the following points: "Open by pulling tab. Avoid touching wound and do not finger the face of the sterilised pad. Place pad over wound, retain hold of short end of bandage, wind remainder firmly and tie in a knot".	
(ii) Medium plain wound dressing, standard no. 14 BPC	2
(iii) Large plain wound dressing, standard no. 15 BPC	2
DRESSING STRIP Elastic adhesive medicated dressing strip BPC, 6 cm × 1m in a packet	1
GAUZE Packet containing one piece of sterile absorbent cotton gauze BP, size 30cm × 90cm	4
GAUZE PADS Packet containing 5 sterile gauze pads BP size 7.5cm × 7.5cm	4

PART 4 – SUNDRIES AND PUBLICATIONS

Note: The packaging for any item on these scales should, where practicable, include the information given in the ordering description for that item.

Name of Item & Ordering Description	Quantities required
EYE BATHS	1

FIRST AID KIT
To be distributed around the ship

The following to be in a damp proof strong canvas bag, satchel, or box, with a strap for carrying:
(1) 4 × triangular bandages, with sides of about 90cm and a base of about 127 cm
(2) 6 × standard dressings no. 8 or 13 BPC
(3) 2 × standard dressings no. 9 or 14 BPC
(4) 2 × extra large sterile unmedicated dressings, 28cm × 17.5cm
(5) 6 medium size safety pins, rustless
(6) 20 assorted elastic adhesive dressing strips medicated BPC
(7) 2 sterile eye pads with attachment
(8) 2 × packages containing 15 grammes sterile cotton wool
(9) 5 pairs of large, disposable, polythene gloves   1

WATER STERILE OR SALINE STERILE
In disposable, sealed containers each holding at least 300ml   2
(This item need only be carried where drinking water is not available)

PUBLICATIONS
(a) "The Ship Captain's Medical Guide" – 21st or latest subsequent edition   1
(b) "First Aid Manual" Published by St John Ambulance/St Andrew's Ambulance Association/The British Red Cross Society 1
(latest edition)
(c) A copy of the Regulations referred to in this Notice   1
(d) A copy of this Notice and subsequent amendments   1

ANNEX 16

GENERAL EXEMPTION

SAIL TRAINING SHIPS

The Secretary of State in exercise of the powers enabling him in that behalf*, hereby exempts sail training ships between 7 metres and 24 metres in length, which are operated commercially at sea, from the following Rules and Regulations wherever appropriate:

(a) The Merchant Shipping (Load Line) Act 1967 and the Merchant Shipping (Load Line) Rules 1968. SI 1968/1053.

(b) The Merchant Shipping (Life Saving Appliances) Regulations 1980. SI 1980/538

(c) The Merchant Shipping (Life Saving Appliances) Regulations 1986. SI 1986/1066

(d) The Merchant Shipping (Fire Appliances) Regulations 1980. SI 1980/544

(e) The Merchant Shipping (Fire Protection) Regulations 1984. SI 1984/1218

(f) The Merchant Shipping (Fire Protection) (Ships built before 25 May 1980) Regulations 1985. SI 1985/1218

(g) The Merchant Shipping (Crew Accommodation) Regulations 1978. SI 1978/795

(h) The Merchant Shipping (Certification of Deck Officers) Regulations 1985. SI 1985/1306

(i) The Merchant Shipping (Medical Stores) Regulations 1986. SI 1986/144

---

*(a) MSA 1906, Section 78
 (b) SI 1980/538, regulation 52
 (c) SI 1986/1066, regulation 27
 (d) SI 1980/544, regulation 76
 (e) SI 1984/1218, regulation 145
 (f) SI 1985/1218, regulation 74
 (g) MSA 1970, section 20(4)
 (h) MSA 1970, section 44
 (i) SI 1986/144, regulation 2(2)

subject to the following conditions:

1. The the ships have been surveyed and inspected and found to comply with the appropriate requirements of the 'Code of Practice for the Construction, Machinery, Equipment, Stability and Survey of Sail Training Ships between 7 metres and 24 metres in length' published by the Marine Directorate of the Department of Transport.

2. That the ships are operated in accordance with the conditions listed on the Sail Training Ship Certificate issued by a Sail Training Ship Certifying Authority.

3. That the medical stores are maintained at the levels and standard required by the Code at all times.

4. This exemption, which may be cancelled or modified by the Department of Transport at any time, shall remain in force until revoked.

Dated this 7th day of February 1990

W.A. GRAHAM

MARINE DIRECTORATE

Department of Transport
for the Secretary of State for
Transport

Printed in the UK for HMSO
Dd291878 C15 4/90 488/2 12521